STANDARD PRACTICES
for
LOW and MEDIUM SPEED
STATIONARY DIESEL and GAS
ENGINES

Published by

DIESEL ENGINE MANUFACTURERS ASSOCIATION

2000 K St., N.W.

Washington 6, D. C.

PRICE, $5.00

2

FOREWORD

In 1930 the "Standards of the Diesel Engine Manufacturers Association" was published for the purpose of removing "some of the misunderstandings of the past which were due to a lack of definitions of terms and practices, and to thereby promote a more intelligent agreement between the buyer and the seller."

Much occurred in the next five years to make desirable the publication of a new edition. So, in 1935 a new "Standard Practices" was published. The Diesel engine had greatly widened its field of use, and the ranks of users, interested consulting engineers, and prospective buyers had increased accordingly. There was a greater need than ever for a clear understanding of the requirements for the Diesel power plant.

The authors of the 1935 and subsequent editions, while recognizing that the general characteristics of all types of Diesel engines are the same, have devoted the contents primarily to heavy duty, low and medium speed engines of the sizes commonly used in stationary power plants. The 1946 and 1951 editions have kept up to date the industry's standard practices with respect to this type of engine.

Recently there has been a growing demand for another revision of a book of standards. Refinements, new developments, and changing procedures have pointed certain sections of "Standard Practices" toward obsolescence, and made desirable considerable editing and the introduction of new material covering such subjects as turbocharging and the use of gaseous and residual fuels.

The result is this present work, "Standard Practices for Low and Medium Speed Stationary Diesel and Gas Engines," produced like its forerunners, with the sole aim to be of service to Diesel and gas engine users, prospective buyers, and consulting engineers. The material in this book represents a consensus of practices developed by engine builders, parts and accessory companies, oil companies, and representatives of other associations and societies having an interest in internal combustion engine power plants of the types under consideration. *It supersedes all previous editions of these standards.*

The existence of, or the adoption of, a standard by DEMA does not in any respect preclude any member or non-member from manufacturing or selling products that differ from these standards.

DIESEL ENGINE MANUFACTURERS ASSOCIATION

Washington, D. C.

Members of the

DIESEL ENGINE MANUFACTURERS ASSOCIATION

July 1, 1958

BALDWIN-LIMA-HAMILTON CORPORATION
Philadelphia, Pa.

CHICAGO PNEUMATIC TOOL COMPANY
New York, N. Y.

CLARK BROS. CO., INC.
Olean, N. Y.

THE COOPER-BESSEMER CORPORATION
Mt. Vernon, O.

ENTERPRISE ENGINE AND MACHINERY CO.
San Francisco, Calif.

FAIRBANKS, MORSE & CO.
Chicago, Ill.

GENERAL MOTORS CORPORATION
Detroit, Mich.

INGERSOLL-RAND COMPANY
New York, N. Y.

NORDBERG MANUFACTURING COMPANY
Milwaukee, Wis.

THE UNION DIESEL ENGINE COMPANY
Oakland, Calif.

THE WHITE MOTOR CO.
Springfield, Ohio

WORTHINGTON CORPORATION
Harrison, N. J.

CONTENTS

INDEX OF DIAGRAMS AND CHARTS

INDEX OF TABLES

STANDARD PRACTICES
for
LOW and MEDIUM SPEED
STATIONARY DIESEL and GAS
ENGINES

CHAPTER ONE

Definitions

The following terms and definitions are used throughout these standards.

Internal Combustion Engine.—An internal combustion engine is any reciprocating engine in which the working medium consists of the products of combustion of the air and fuel supplied. Throughout this book the term "engine" will refer to reciprocating internal combustion engines other than gasoline engines.

Diesel Engine.—A Diesel engine is an internal combustion engine in which the fuel is ignited entirely by the heat resulting from the compression of the air supplied for combustion.

**Gas Engine.*—A gas engine is an internal combustion engine that operates on a combustible gas fuel and in which the gas is ignited by an electric spark. A gas engine may have a compression pressure lower than, or equal to, that of a Diesel engine.

Oil-Diesel Engine.—An oil-Diesel engine is one which operates on fuel oil injected after compression is practically completed.

Gas-Diesel Engine.—A gas-Diesel is an engine which operates on a combustible gas as primary fuel and in which the ignition of the gas is accomplished or aided by pilot-oil fuel injected after compression is practically completed. The gas fuel may be compressed in the engine cylinder with the air or it may be compressed separately and injected into the combustion chamber near the end of the compression stroke.

Dual Fuel Diesel Engine. A dual fuel Diesel engine is one which may be operated as an oil-Diesel or a gas-Diesel engine or a combination of both, and is equipped with controls or parts to permit operating as one or the other.

Surface-Ignition Engine.—A surface-ignition engine is an internal combustion engine in which the ignition of the fuel is not accomplished solely by the heat resulting from the compression of the air supplied for combustion, but partly (or entirely) by another heat supplying agency or agencies, such as an uncooled tube, bulb or plate, or an electric resistance coil. In the strict sense, engines with spark ignition might come within the limits of this definition,

---

* NOTE: Many makes of spark-fired gas engines are built to operate on Diesel compression ratios and may be converted to dual fuel engines when fuel oil injection equipment and dual fuel parts are added to replace the spark ignition system. Conversely many makes of dual fuel engines may be converted to spark-fired gas engines when a spark ignition system and gas engine parts are added to replace the dual fuel injection equipment.

but are specifically excluded. Other names by which this type engine has been called are hot bulb, hot head and semi-Diesel.

Cycle.—A cycle in an internal combustion engine is the complete series of events wherein induction and compression of air, burning of fuel, expansion and expulsion of the working medium are accomplished before repetition occurs.

Four-Cycle Engine.—An engine completing one cycle in four strokes or two revolutions is called a four-cycle engine. The cyclic events are designated by the following strokes: (1) Induction or suction stroke; (2) Compression stroke; (3) Expansion stroke, and (4) Exhaust stroke.

Two-Cycle Engine.—An engine completing one cycle in two strokes or one revolution is called a two-cycle engine. The cyclic events are designated by the following strokes: (1) Induction and compression stroke, and (2) Expansion and exhaust stroke.

Single Acting Engine.—An engine that utilizes the working medium on one side of a single piston is called a single acting engine.

Double Acting Engine.—An engine that utilizes the working medium on both sides of a single piston is called a double acting engine.

Opposed Piston Engine.—An engine utilizing the working medium simultaneously on two pistons in the same cylinder is called an opposed piston engine.

Trunk Piston Engine.—A trunk piston engine is an engine in which the connecting rod is connected directly to the wristpin in the piston. In this type of engine, the side thrust caused by the angularity of the connecting rod is taken by the piston bearing against the cylinder wall.

Crosshead Engine.—A crosshead engine is an engine in which the connecting rod is connected to a crosshead traveling in guides, and the crosshead in turn is connected to the corresponding piston. The side thrust caused by the angularity of the connecting rod is taken by the crosshead and guides.

Air Injection.—The term air injection refers to a method of introducing the fuel charge into the power cylinder of an engine. By this method a quantity of high pressure air forces its way through a mechanically operated valve into the power cylinder by virtue of its margin of pressure over the compression pressure in the power cylinder, and carries with it the fuel charge.

Mechanical Injection.—The term mechanical injection refers to a method of introducing the fuel charge into the power cylinder of an engine. The injection system is completely filled with liquid fuel, and the fuel charge is injected into the combustion chamber under pressure built up by a fuel pump. Mechanical injection systems may be subdivided into the following:

(a) Pump-timed injection system, in which the fuel is injected into the engine cylinder directly by the action of the fuel injection pump plunger. The action of the pump both meters and times the injection of the fuel.

(b) Pump-timed injection system, with distributor, in which the fuel pump both times the injection and meters the fuel charge. The distributor is a selective device which determines the particular cylinder to which the fuel charge is delivered.

(c) Common-rail system, in which a fuel pump supplies fuel to a header, called the common-rail, at a pressure above the cylinder pressure of the engine, the fuel being passed from this common-rail to each cylinder in turn at the proper time through mechanically operated valves.

(d) Controlled pressure-injection system, in which a fuel pump supplies fuel to a header or distributor at varying pressures, the fuel being metered to each power cylinder through injectors by mechanically operated valves which reduce the line pressure to a low value after each injection.

(e) Low pressure distributor injection system, in which a multi-plunger pump or single pump plunger with a distributor delivers the fuel to multiple injectors, the timing and injection being accomplished by the cam actuation of the injectors, and the pump and distributor serving only as a metering device at relatively low fuel pressure.

Scavenging Air.—The term scavenging air refers to air at low pressure that is used for forcing the burnt gases out of the power cylinder of an engine during the exhaust period and, by this displacement, for furnishing a supply of fresh air for the cycle following. Scavenging air is sometimes employed for four-cycle engines and always for two-cycle engines.

a. The air may be compressed by any of the following methods:

(1) Separate scavenging, by which the air is compressed in a scavenging compressor or blower driven by an independent source of power.

(2) Integral scavenging, by which the air is compressed in a scavenging compressor or blower direct-connected, geared, or belted to the engine scavenged.

(3) Under-piston scavenging, by which the air is compressed on the underside of the power piston in a chamber which is separated from the crankcase of the engine. The upstrokes of the power piston draw air into this chamber from the atmosphere and the downstrokes compress the air so drawn in, with suitable air valving provided.

(4) Crankcase scavenging, by which the air is drawn from the atmosphere into individual crank chambers, one for each cylinder, by the upstrokes of the power piston and compressed in the respective crank chambers by the downstrokes of the piston, with suitable air valving provided.

b. Scavenging air may be introduced into the power cylinder by any of the following methods:

(1) Port scavenging, by which the scavenging air enters the cylinder of a two-cycle engine through a series of ports in the cylinder wall and forces the burnt gases through another series of ports into the exhaust line.

(2) Valve scavenging, by which the scavenging air enters the engine cylinder through a mechanically operated valve or valves, usually located in the cylinder head, and forces the burnt gases into the exhaust line, usually through a series of ports in the cylinder wall.

(3) Port and valve scavenging, in which the scavenging air enters the engine cylinder through a series of ports in the cylinder wall and forces the burnt gases through mechanically operated valve or valves in the cylinder head.

Supercharging.—The term supercharging refers to the practice of supplying the intake of an engine with air at a density greater than the density of the surrounding atmosphere, this increased density being retained in the cylinders at the start of the compression stroke.

The method of supercharging falls in two general classifications, namely:

(a) Turbine driven blower—With this method the exhaust gases from the engine cylinders are used to drive an exhaust gas turbine direct connected to a blower that supplies air to the engine intake manifold. There are no mechanical drive connections between the engine and turbine.

(b) Mechanically driven blower—The blower supplying air to the intake manifold may be driven direct from the engine or separately driven by an electric motor or other suitable prime mover. When separately driven, the additional power required to drive the blower is taken into account in determining the net brake horsepower rating of the engine.

It should be noted that while scavenging air is supplied to two-cycle engines at a density greater than atmospheric, this practice does not supercharge an engine unless arrangements are made to retain air of increased density in the power cylinders, after the exhaust ports or valves close.

Force Feed Lubrication.—Force feed lubrication is that system of lubrication in which the lubricating oil is delivered under pressure produced directly by a metering pump, usually called a force feed lubricator.

Gravity Feed Lubrication.—Gravity feed lubrication is that system of lubrication in which the lubricating oil is delivered under action of gravity from an elevated supply.

Pressure Lubrication.—Pressure lubrication is that system of lubrication in which lubricating oil is delivered under controlled pressure produced by a non-metering pump.

Drop Feed Lubrication.—Drop feed lubrication is that system of lubrication in which the lubricating oil delivery is metered by regulating the number of drops per minute as observed through a sight feed.

Starting Air Compressor.—A starting air compressor is a compressor used to supply air at a pressure sufficient to start the engine. This air is stored in receivers sometimes called starting air tanks or starting air bottles. Compressors of this type may be single- or multi-stage.

Injection Air Compressor.—An injection air compressor is a compressor operated to furnish air at a pressure sufficient to inject fuel into the engine which it serves. Because of the high air pressure required, injection-air compressors are of the multi-stage type, with intercoolers between stages and an aftercooler following the high pressure stage.

Displacement.—

(a) Engine Displacement per minute—The displacement per minute of an engine is the volume in cubic feet per minute which is swept by the piston (or all of the pistons, if more than one) during the power strokes, and is equal to: Number of cylinders times the area of the piston in square feet times the stroke in feet times the number of power strokes per cylinder per minute.

(b) Engine Piston Displacement—Engine piston displacement is the cylinder volume in cubic inches swept by the pistons and is equal to: Number of cylinders times the area of each piston in square inches times the stroke in inches.

(c) Compressor Displacement and Capacity[1]—

(1) Displacement of a compressor is the volume displaced per unit of time and is usually expressed in cubic feet per minute. In a reciprocating compressor it equals the net area of the compressor piston multiplied by the length of stroke and by the number of strokes per minute. The displacement rating of a multi-stage compressor is the displacement of the low pressure cylinder only.

---

[1] Reprinted from COMPRESSED AIR HANDBOOK, Second Edition, Copyright 1954 by the compressed Air and Gas Institute, 122 E. 42nd St., New York 17, N. Y., and published by McGraw Hill Book Company.

(2) Capacity (Actual Delivery). The capacity of an air or gas compressor is the actual quantity of air or gas compressed and delivered expressed in cubic feet per minute at conditions of temperature and pressure prevailing at the compressor intake.

(3) Volumetric Efficiency is the ratio of the capacity of the compressor to the displacement of the compressor.

Horsepower.—One horsepower (hp) (U. S. or British) is a rate of doing work equal to 33,000 ft-lb per minute. [One horsepower (metric) is equal to 75.0 kg-m per second.] One U. S. or British horsepower is larger than one metric horsepower. The relationship between the two is as follows:

One U. S. horsepower equals 1.014 metric horsepower.
One metric horsepower equals 0.9863 U. S. horsepower.

Indicated Horsepower.—The indicated horsepower (ihp) of an engine cylinder is the horsepower developed in the cylinder. It can be determined from the mean indicated pressure (see paragraph below), the engine speed and the cylinder dimensions. The formula is:

$$ihp = \frac{mip \times L \times A \times N}{33,000}$$

where

mip = mean indicated pressure, psi.
L = stroke of piston, ft.
A = the net piston area, sq. in.
N = number of power strokes per minute.

Mean Indicated Pressure.—The mean indicated pressure (mip) is the algebraic sum of the mean pressures in pounds per square inch acting on the piston for each stroke during one complete cycle. Pressures are positive when acting in the direction the piston is moving and negative when opposite.

Brake Horsepower.—The brake horsepower (bhp) of an engine is the horsepower delivered by the shaft at the output end. The name is derived from the fact that it is determined by a brake. The formula is:

$$bhp = \frac{2 \times \pi \times r \times rpm \times W}{33,000}$$

where

r = distance between the shaft center and the point of application of the weight to the brake arm, ft.
rpm = revolutions per minute of the brake shaft.
W = effective weight on the brake arm, lb.
π = 3.1416

Brake Mean Effective Pressure.—Brake mean effective pressure (bmep) is:

$$bmep = \frac{bhp \times 33,000}{L \times A \times N}$$

where

bhp = brake horsepower per cylinder and L, A, and N, are as in the foregoing paragraph.

Piston Speed.—The piston speed of an engine is the total feet of travel made by each piston in one minute. The formula is:

Piston Speed = stroke in feet $\times$ rpm $\times$ 2

High Heating Value.—The high heating value (hhv) of a fuel is the heat produced in Btu by the complete combustion of a unit quantity at standard conditions of temperature, pressure and humidity based on all the products of combustion being cooled to the initial conditions of temperature, pressure and humidity.

Unit Quantity.—For gaseous fuels the unit quantity is one cubic foot at the standard conditions of:

1. A temperature of 60 F.
2. A pressure of 30 in. Hg (14.73 psia), the mercury to be at the ice point temperature (32 F) and subject to an acceleration of gravity of 32.174 ft per sec per sec.
3. A condition of complete water vapor saturation.

For liquid fuels the unit quantity is one pound at 60 F.

Low Heating Value.—The low heating value (lhv) of a fuel is the heat produced in Btu by the complete combustion of a unit quantity at standard conditions of temperature, pressure and humidity, less the latent heat of the water vapor condensed, based on all the products of combustion being cooled to the initial conditions of temperature, pressure and humidity.

Engine Assembly.—This covers an engine complete with all essential apparatus, headers and piping normally part of the engine as required for: fuel introduction, air induction, supercharging, ignition, scavenging, exhaust, lubrication and piston cooling. Specifically an engine assembly includes apparatus to meter, carburate or inject the fuel delivered to it at normal operating supply pressure including booster fuel pump when attached to the engine; to supply induction air; to provide injection air or gas if the engine is of the air or gas injection type; to compress induction air if engine is pressure scavenged or supercharged; to provide ignition; to circulate lubricating oil throughout the engine lubrication system, including pumps, gravity tank, oil cooler, strainers and mechanical force feed lubricator; as pertinent to the particular engine unit.

Plant Auxiliaries.—This covers apparatus not included in the engine assembly as defined in above paragraph. Such plant auxiliaries include power consuming apparatus for circulating coolants through all jackets and heat exchange equipment. They also include cooling fans, apparatus for compressing starting air, conditioning and transferring fuel and lubricating oil, or any other power consuming equipment not included under engine assembly. Plant auxiliaries may also include non-power consuming equipment such as exhaust mufflers, air filters, air intake silencers, etc.

Indicated Thermal Efficiency.—The indicated thermal efficiency of an engine is equal to the ratio of the heat equivalent of one horsepower hour to the number of heat units actually supplied per indicated horsepower hour. This may be calculated from either the high or low heat value of the fuel, with proper designation as to which value is used.

Brake Thermal Efficiency.—The brake thermal efficiency of an engine is equal to the ratio of the heat equivalent of one horsepower hour to the number of heat units actually supplied per brake horsepower hour. This may be calculated from either the high or low heat value of the fuel, with proper designation as to which value is used.

Mechanical Efficiency.—Mechanical efficiency is the ratio of brake horsepower to indicated horsepower.

Horsepower Ratings.—All horsepower ratings herein are net horsepower after adjustment for auxiliaries, as explained in Chapter Two.

The Diesel Engine Manufacturers Association hereby recognizes as standard the definitions on page 208 of fundamental units and constants. The abbreviations shown throughout this text are those appearing in the Appendix, Table 16.

Power plant building of the Iowa Electric Light and Power Company, De Witt, Iowa, housing 2000 kw of four-cycle Diesel generating sets.

CHAPTER TWO

Performance and Equipment

In the course of development of internal combustion engines in this country, certain practices and usages have become so universal as to be generally accepted by not only the builders of such engines but by purchasers and users, consulting engineers, and others interested in this industry. These practices include yardsticks for the measurement of performance, horsepower output, etc., and provide a basis for a common understanding between purchaser and manufacturer.

Sea Level Ratings.—The possibilities open to the designer of the combustion space and the fuel injection system are so many that the purchaser or consulting engineer should not set a rigid limit for the brake mean effective pressure rating (pounds per square inch) for either two or four-cycle engines. To attempt to set such limits would only hamper progress. The sea level rating of an engine is the net brake horsepower that the engine will deliver continuously when in good operating condition and located at an altitude of not over 1500 ft above sea level, with atmospheric temperature not over 90 F and barometric pressure not less than 28.25 in. of mercury. Engine manufacturers offer engines with a sufficiently conservative sea level rating so that the engines will be capable of delivering an output of 10 percent in excess of full load rating, with safe operating temperatures, for two continuous hours, but not to exceed a total of two hours, out of any 24 consecutive hours of operation.

The net brake horsepower referred to above is the horsepower delivered at the engine coupling of an Engine Assembly as defined in Chapter One, page 21. Apparatus listed in Plant Auxiliaries, as defined in Chapter One are not included in the net brake horsepower. In calculating the bmep of an engine the net brake horsepower, as defined above, is used.

Ratings at Higher Altitudes.—Manufacturers' sea level ratings and reserve capacity apply for all altitudes up to 1500 ft above sea level, with atmospheric temperatures of not more than 90 F and barometric pressure of not less than 28.25 in. of mercury. This is a purely practical provision to make it unnecessary to correct engine ratings for the majority of installations. The power which any naturally aspirated internal combustion engine is capable of delivering decreases as the altitude increases. The lower atmospheric pressure and density at higher altitudes causes this decrease in engine capacity because of the resultant lower quantity of oxygen available for combustion of the fuel in the engine cylinder.

The resultant net brake horsepower ratings at various altitudes of naturally aspirated and non-supercharged engines are expressed in percent of their sea level ratings on the curve shown in Fig. 1.

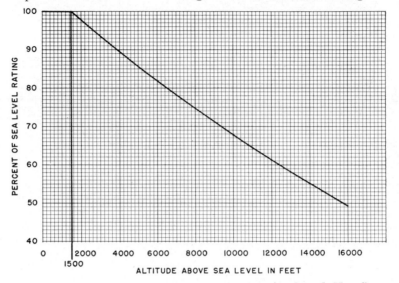

Fig. 1. Altitude Ratings for Naturally Aspirated and Non-Supercharged Engines Expressed in Percent of Their Sea Level Ratings.

Ratings at Elevated Temeratures.

—The following discussion applies only to naturally aspirated and non-supercharged engines not furnished with any intake air cooling equipment. As stated above, sea level ratings and altitude ratings are based on atmospheric temperatures at engine air intake of not more than 90 F. The power which any engine is capable of delivering decreases as the intake air temperature increases. The higher air intake temperature decreases the horsepower capacity of an engine because hotter air is less dense, resulting in a smaller quantity of oxygen available for combustion of fuel in the engine cylinder. Very few localities exceed 90 F air temperature for more than a few hours on a few days in the year. Therefore the practice has grown to make engine ratings apply to temperatures up to 90 F for atmospheric intake air for the engine and apply derating only for higher temperatures. If such intake air supply temperature exceeds 90 F, the engine capacity is reduced in accordance with the curve in Fig. 2 in addition to any reduction due to altitude.

Effects of Supercharging and Inlet Air Cooling on Derating.

—The use of superchargers and turbochargers as well as intake air cooling equipment makes it possible to recover varying amounts of the loss in brake horsepower which otherwise would result in operation at altitudes above 1500 ft or atmospheric temperatures above 90 F. Because of the many variables, any formula for making derating calculations under these conditions becomes so involved as to make its use impracticable. It is for this reason that the curves in Fig. 1 and Fig. 2 have been confined to naturally aspirated and non-supercharged engines having no intake air cooling equipment. Engine manufacturers with full knowledge of operating conditions will rate their engines in accordance with the compensating equipment furnished. To offset altitude effect, engine builders are using various means of supercharging. The buyer should make certain that proper allowance is made in the net engine rating for any additional power required by separately driven superchargers and their accessories.

In moving an engine to a new elevation or different maximum temperature conditions the manufacturer should be consulted as to the proper rating for such new conditions.

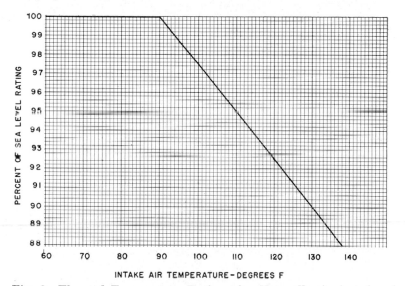

Fig. 2. Elevated Temperature Ratings for Naturally Aspirated and Non-Supercharged Engines Having No Intake Air Cooling Equipment, Expressed in Percent of Their Sea Level Ratings.

Brake Horsepower Capacity and Fuel Consumption Guarantees.—Engine builders' guarantees of brake horsepower capacity and fuel consumption are usually based upon tests conducted by the builder on his test floor. Such tests are conducted on development models or original models of a production series and shop tests of subsequent engines are optional with the manufacturer. Test setups for the larger engines which are usually dismantled for shipment are cumbersome and expensive; therefore, they are often tested in the field after installation rather than shop tested.

Brake horsepower capacity guarantees for engines operating at 0 to 1500 ft altitude are generally made contingent upon an air intake pressure of not less than 28.25 in. of mercury and air intake temperature of not more than 90 F. When tested in the field after installation at higher altitudes and/or higher air temperatures, the brake horsepower for naturally aspirated and non-supercharged engines having no intake air cooling should be reduced in accordance with the curves in Fig. 1 and Fig. 2 and for other engines the manufacturer's ratings for such field conditions should be used.

Fuel oil consumption guarantees are usually made in pounds per net brake horsepower hour at one-half, three-quarter and full load (sea level rating or altitude rating) when operating at rated revolutions per minute. Gas-burning and dual fuel Diesel engine gas consumption guarantees are made in Btu per net brake horsepower hour and are based on low heat value. Fuel oil and pilot oil guarantees are based on a high (gross) heat value of 19,350 Btu per pound, which is an average Diesel fuel oil. When gas-Diesel and dual fuel Diesel engines operate with gas as a primary fuel, the fuel consumption guarantees are made on a basis of the total fuel (gas at low heat value plus pilot oil at high heat value) consumed by the engine in Btu per net brake horsepower hour. The pilot oil rate is usually stated in the guarantee and is expressed in Btu high heat value per net brake horsepower hour. If, during the acceptance test, the pilot oil rate is less than the guarantee, the gas consumption rate should be permitted to be increased accordingly so that the total fuel consumption in Btu remains the same regardless of the actual pilot oil setting. This is necessary because such engines' overall efficiencies remain the same over a fairly broad range of pilot oil quantity. All sea level fuel consumption guarantees are contingent upon the following conditions:

1. Intake air temperature not over 90 F, unless the use of combustion air cooling permits a higher maximum atmospheric intake air temperature for rating.

2. Barometric pressure of intake air not less than 28.25 in. of mercury.

3. Fuel to conform to the engine builders' specifications as set forth in his bid or tender.

4. Engine jacket water and lubricating oil temperatures to be within plus or minus 10 F of normal temperatures specified in engine builder's bid or tender.

All heat engines utilize only the low heat of whatever fuel is used. The high heat value of fuels containing hydrogen includes some heat not available for conversion into work in any internal combustion engine. Due to the greater ease and accuracy with which the high heat value of fuel oil can be determined, oil refiners and distributors sell oil on the high heat basis exclusively. Furthermore, the difference between high and low heat values of fuel oils is a fairly constant percentage. It is for this reason fuel oil consumption guarantees are based on the high heat value.

For gaseous fuels, however, the percentage difference between the high and low heat values may range from 0 to approximately 15 percent because of varying hydrogen and moisture content. This is the reason gas consumption guarantees are based on the low heat value of saturated gas.

All fuel consumption quantity rates should be corrected for any deviation in the thermal value of the fuel used from that stated in the guarantee.

Engine manufacturers do not guarantee fuel consumption for one-quarter load. There are several good technical reasons for this. Small differences in cooling water temperature or in internal friction have a disproportionate effect at such low load, especially in the case of a new engine. Therefore tests for quarter-load fuel consumption are inaccurate and not reproducible. Generator builders do not make quarter-load efficiency guarantees so the results cannot be expressed in terms of fuel per kilowatt hour.

Fuel Consumption Guarantees for Engines Derated for Altitude and/or Elevated Air Temperatures.—Many variables affect fuel consumption rates for engines derated for altitude above 1500 ft and/or air intake temperature above 90 F. Therefore, it is not practical to apply a standard correction to all engine builders' sea level fuel consumption rates. Under such conditions the derated engine fuel consumption guarantees must be furnished by the engine manufacturer.

When the purchase specifications require shop tests in lieu of or in addition to field tests, engine builders offer fuel consumption guarantees for the normal sea level rating as well as for the high altitude and/or elevated air intake temperature conditions.

Field Tests for Horsepower Capacity and Fuel Consumption. If the buyer of an engine so requests, a guarantee test for horsepower capacity and fuel consumption may be made after the engine is installed in its ultimate location. When more elaborate tests are required by the buyer, it is recommended that such tests be conducted in accordance with the Field Test Code presented in Chapter Eighteen of this book. Such tests are costly. Obviously, unless such tests are paid for by buyers requesting them, the entire cost of field testing must come from the whole body of buyers of engines. It is, therefore, equitable that each buyer requesting any field test be required to bear the fair and full cost of it, including the furnishing of (a) all apparatus required; (b) all labor necessary for the installation and operation of such apparatus, for the observation and recording of test data, and for the calculation of test results, and (c) all fuel, lubricating oil, water, supplies and the appropriate steady loads required for the tests requested. Such fuel and lubricating oils furnished should be in conformity with the engine builder's specifications for the type and speed of the engine to be tested.

Lubricating Oil Consumption.—The same engine if installed in several plants in succession would show different rates of lubricating oil consumption, so material is the influence of plant conditions and operation on lubrication requirements. These are beyond the engine builder's control and the purchaser should not request more than an estimate of what the lubricating oil consumption should be.

All reputable oil suppliers can furnish the proper lubricants for almost any type of machinery. The user of the engine should consult the engine manufacturer, giving him the names of the suppliers from whom he wishes to purchase his lubricants. The engine builder will then indicate the oils of such suppliers that appear suitable.

Governor Performance.—As its name implies, the function of a governing system is to govern, or regulate the fuel supply of an engine to control speed under varying load conditions. The need for such regulation varies with the driven equipment and load conditions. For industrial electric drives involving a single generator where constant voltage is not important, for non-electric drives, and where loading is relatively uniform there is usually little need for speed regulation closer than 5 to 6 percent (variation between full load and no load speed in percentage of full load speed). For multiple electric drives such as municipal plants where time clocks and other constant frequency equipment is involved, much closer regulation is required.

Two types of governors are commonly furnished: (1) non-isochronous, or (2) isochronous, depending on the service intended. These may be further divided into centrifugally-powered or relay-powered. Centrifugally-powered refers to the standard mechanical governor in which power to operate the fuel control linkage is supplied by the flyweights. Relay-powered governors refer to those in which power for operating the fuel control linkage is supplied by a suitable relay which may be actuated by hydraulic, electric, or electronic means.

Non-isochronous governors may be either centrifugally-powered or relay-powered, while isochronous governors are always of the relay type.

The following performance is considered satisfactory for the centrifugal type:

1. The governor will control the engine speed to 5 to 8 percent of the rated speed upon gradual load changes from no load to full load, or vice versa.

2. For sudden changes in load within the limits of engine rating, not exceeding one-quarter rated load, the momentary speed change does not exceed the normal no-load full-load percentage regulation. This momentary speed change is in percent of speed at the instant of load change.

3. Under constant load there should be no hunting; with changing load there should be no sustained oscillations of speed or power output following a load change.

The following performance is usually available and considered satisfactory for governors of the non-isochronous relay-powered type:

1. The governor will control the engine speed to 2 to 8 percent of the rated full load speed upon gradual load changes from no load to full load, or vice versa, the percentage of regulation being adjustable during engine operation.

2. Where an engine is intended for parallel operation, the momentary speed change for sudden changes in load within the limits of engine rating, not exceeding one-quarter rated load, will not exceed 5 percent of the speed at instant of load change.

3. Under constant load there should be no hunting; with changing load there should be no sustained oscillations of speed or power output following a load change.

For isochronous governors of the relay type with adjustable speed regulation* the performance should be the same as outlined above, except that the governor will control engine speed to 0 to 3 percent upon gradual load changes.

A further discussion of governing will be found in Chapter Four.

Parallel Operation.—It is the practice of engine builders to provide engine generator units with properly sized flywheels to enable them to operate satisfactorily alone, in parallel with any large power transmission system, or in parallel with any number of identical engines of the same rpm. In addition, new engine generator units can usually be designed (by proper flywheel application) to operate satisfactorily in parallel with existing engine generator units of different characteristics and/or rpm which already parallel successfully, and provided existing units are inherently suitable for parallel operation in an infinite system. Complete information on the existing units must be made available.

Parallel operation with every combination of units in an existing power system is not always possible, as with a variety of generating unit speeds and electrical characteristics there may be some interference between certain combinations of units. In such cases the best possible flywheel selection is made and the engine manufacturer advises the buyer the unit combinations that may or may not be satisfactorily paralleled.

Failure to parallel successfully cannot be proven by the behavior of switchboard instruments which may not be properly damped. It is essential that a clear distinction be made between instrument swings due to load swings which are not a measure of parallel

---

* Isochronous governors without speed regulation adjustment may be furnished where such characteristics are suitable. (See also Frequency Regulations, Chapt. 4.)

operation, and swings due to actual inter-unit or inter-plant paralleling difficulties.

A further discussion of parallel operation will be found in Chapters Four and Fourteen.

Torsional Vibration and Critical Speeds.—The engine builder, when furnishing all the driven equipment, is responsible for the design of the shafting, bearings, connections, etc., between the engine and the driven equipment with respect to torsional vibrations. When the driven equipment is furnished by anyone other than the engine builder, it is the buyer's responsibility to furnish the engine builder accurate and complete information on the driven equipment so that the engine builder can design and recommend connection details. The buyer should understand that delays in supplying this information may affect shipments and cause added expense due to changes which may be required.

If a generator is to operate in parallel with existing units, necessary data on such units must be furnished by the buyer to the engine builder so that the latter can determine flywheel requirements for paralleling at the same time he is analyzing the torsional problem.

For further discussion of torsional vibration, see Chapter Five.

Finish.—Engines are usually given one coat of primer or filler, and finished with one coat of paint of the engine builder's standard color, unless otherwise agreed upon.

Stationary Engine Equipment.—The minimum amount of equipment which should be required with a stationary engine should not include any apparatus which might require different treatment for different installations. With this precept in mind, the following list of minimum equipment is offered to enable the purchaser to check the engine manufacturer's proposal. Whenever the items listed are required by the design of any engine, they should be furnished with it, but items not so required should not be furnished. For instance, it would be superfluous to include piston-cooling equipment with an engine having dry pistons.

CHECK LIST OF MINIMUM ENGINE EQUIPMENT AND SERVICE FOR STATIONARY ENGINES

Engine flywheel (except in the case of flywheel type generator).

Extension shaft and outboard bearings if required.

Piping on engine to inlet and outlet connections, including all non-standard companion flanges.

Exhaust manifold or its equivalent.

Air inlet manifold or its equivalent.

Combustion air cooling equipment, if required.

Blower and its driving equipment for engines which are supercharged.

Scavenging air equipment for two-cycle engines.

Ignition equipment on engine for spark ignition gas engines, but not including ignition battery or charger.

Lubricating oil strainer or its equivalent.

Fuel oil strainer or its equivalent.

Fuel oil booster pump if required.

Lubricating oil sump tank if required.

Force-feed lubricator if required.

Lubricating oil pumps and coolers if required.

Piston cooling oil pump and cooler if required.

Pump for circulating lubricating oil before starting and after stopping oil-cooled-piston engine if required.

Lubricating oil pressure gages for pressure system.

Engine cooling water pressure gages if required.

Thermometers for lubricating oil to and from engine, and piston-cooling oil if required.

Thermometers for engine cooling water supply and discharge.

Compression release valves.

Suitable governing equipment.

Synchronizing device, hand or electrically operated (for generator units) where necessary.

Flywheel barring device, hand or power operated.

A set of special non-commercial tools for each installation (not duplicated for more than one engine per engine room). (See page 34, "Wrenches and Tools.")

The builder's standard set of spare parts.

Engine platforms and steps or stairs if required, but not including interconnecting platforms.

Drilled and tapped holes for exhaust temperature measuring devices, but not including such devices.

Drilled and tapped holes for attachment of an indicator, but not including the indicator, indicator valves, or reducing motion.

Foundation bolts, nuts, and anchor plates, including those for generator and exciter, and for main and auxiliary engine equipment if these units are furnished, but not including sleeves or casings.

Instruction book for operator.

Foundation blueprints for good soil.

Profile prints showing size and location of piping on engine, to which buyer connects.

Diagrammatic prints showing recommended arrangement of typical station piping.

Engine part lists.

CHAPTER THREE

Engine Construction

Engine builders of this country have been, and still are most active in carrying on intensive engineering development programs. All of these programs have not been conducted along the same lines. The different methods of engineering approach, productive of this variety, present no real inconsistency, since all have brought about the same result—a modern unit of high economy and reliability.

Any limitation in specifications to exclude one or more standard makes of engines because of variations from a specific type only places the prospective buyer at a disadvantage by limiting his choice. The shrewdest buying strategy specifies only the requirements to be met because of the plant conditions, and requires the bidder to submit detailed specifications covering the engine or engines and the accessories offered. The suggested specifications in Chapter Nineteen take such a method into account by presenting blank forms to be filled out by bidders. The form on pages 186-189 is suggested as covering all data essential for purposes of comparison of engines. No specification or tabulation can eliminate the need for the exercise of experienced judgment in the selection of the best bid.

There is more than one acceptable treatment of design for a modern engine. Some manufacturers build engines of two-cycle type, others of four-cycle type, and some make engines of both types concurrently. Both types of engines have attained a high level of performance and economy. There are many other different treatments of design which produce equivalent results. Some of these will be discussed in this chapter.

Attached Pumps.—Some engines, usually the smaller ones, have circulating water pumps built-in (that is, mounted on the engine itself and driven from the engine by gear or chain drive). Larger engines usually are designed without built-in water pumps and, therefore, require the installation of motor-driven pumps. Some two-cycle engines are constructed with built-in scavenging pumps or blowers, others require the use of motor-driven equipment.

Flywheel.—The dimensions and weights of flywheels of engines cannot be determined accurately until the equipment to be driven is first selected, and the necessary engineering data pertaining to the driven equipment are analyzed and evaluated with respect to parallel operation of alternating current generators and torsional vibration. (See Chapter Five on "Torsional Vibrations and Critical Speeds.")

Engine flywheels may be of one- or two-piece construction and must have suitable flywheel effect for the purpose intended. Some types of engines require very little flywheel effect, and this may be provided by the generator rotor. Generators with weighted rotors are specified as flywheel type, or weighted rotor type, as distinguished from standard engine type, but both types as offered by reputable generator manufacturers are of essentially the same design.

Specifications should be so written as to permit the engine builder to select the type and weight of flywheel for his engine as intended for a given service, or to omit the flywheel if the Wk² of the driven equipment is sufficient to produce the necessary flywheel effect.

Engine Extension Shafts.—The length and diameter of extension shafts of engines vary with the type and speed of the engines, the type of generator or other driven equipment, and the critical speed or torsional vibration conditions indicated by calculations after the necessary data covering the driven equipment have been assembled and analyzed. Torsional vibration conditions may require the shifting of the generator or other directly mounted and driven equipment toward the flywheel or the outboard bearing. Under certain conditions it may be necessary to make a slight change in the diameter of the extension shaft to provide a smoothly running unit. Flywheel type generators usually are mounted on short extension shafts, whereas standard engine type generators require longer extension shafts. The exact dimensions of the extension shaft, therefore, cannot be determined until after the driven equipment is selected and the necessary engineering data analyzed.

Flywheel Barring Device.—Flywheel barring devices are required for rotating an engine to its starting position or for adjustment and repair purposes. There are three types of barring devices used—manual, pneumatic, and electric. The use of barring devices is so infrequent that the furnishing of unusually expensive apparatus is not warranted. The engine builder may be relied upon to furnish flywheel barring mechanism of proper type for a specified engine.

Smaller engines are generally furnished with manually operated flywheel barring devices. Electrically or pneumatically operated gear is generally used with sizes that would require two men to rotate the engine if a manually operated device were used. Pneumatic devices are actuated by air under pressure from the starting air tanks. In the larger sized engines where the use of an electrically operated barring device is justified, some manufacturers furnish it as standard equipment.

Sub-Bases.—Generally, engine generator sets are mounted directly on concrete foundations. In the case of units of smaller size, sub-bases are sometimes used to permit (a) use of a simpler concrete foundation, and (b) the shipment of a completely assembled unit. Sub-bases are of several different types, such as (a) integral extension of the engine bedplate to provide mounting for the generator, (b) separate base extending under engine and generator, (c) separate base under engine only. Sub-bases may also be used when the driven equipment is other than an electrical generator. Use of a sub-base in no way eliminates the need for aligning prime mover with the driven equipment after being placed on the foundation.

Engine Platforms.—The difference in engine design (that is, height of controls from floor level, accessibility of parts for removal or adjustment) is responsible for a variety of engine platform arrangements. Some types and sizes of engines do not require platforms on both sides, whereas others would not be sufficiently accessible without them. It is, therefore, well to leave such details to the engine builder. Where two or more engines are installed, the buyer may wish interconnecting runways between platforms. These can be furnished as extras by the engine builder. The buyer's drawings in such cases should show the exact locations of all engines and interconnecting runways with any additional ladders desired, as well as any supports to be made available by the buyer for these runways.

Right- and Left-Hand Engines.—Specifications covering plants to contain two engines sometimes call for one of these to be right-hand, the other left-hand. Such a specification means, if two adjacent engines are so arranged that the flywheels (generators) are side by side, with the engine operating controls located nearest the aisle between the units and exhaust manifolds outboard, then when looking toward the engines from a point between the flywheels, the right-hand engine will be to the viewer's right, and the left-hand engine to the left. There may have been a reason for such an arrangement before the days of remote governor control, but with the common use of such control and the very little attention needed by engines when running, it is usually unnecessary. Such a specification requires one of the engines to be non-standard, with the loss of interchangeability that this means. In any case, any advantage is lost if and when a third unit is installed.

Wrenches and Tools.—It is usual practice to include in standard equipment all necessary special wrenches and tools required for a specific engine but not to furnish any wrenches or tools that can be purchased readily on the open market. Most power plants have all necessary standard wrenches and tools for general purposes, and duplication would be superfluous. Duplications of special wrenches are not necessary if two or more similar engines are installed. The list of special wrenches and tools for engines varies with the type, size and make of engine. No detailed specification of a standard list can be made.

Wrench boards are not usually furnished as standard equipment. In cases where specifications call for a wrench board, the consulting engineer should show the type, dimensions, materials of construction and finish, in order that bids may be requested of manufacturers of such equipment. In general it is much more desirable to have wrench boards made in local carpentry shops after the full complement of wrenches and tools has been selected and the most suitable location of the wrench board has been determined.

Engine Spare Parts.—Spare parts included in the list of standard equipment of engines necessarily vary with the type of engines specified; consequently, a standard list of spares cannot properly be specified. Engine builders' specifications should list in detail the spare parts included as standard equipment. In cases where such a detailed list does not accompany the proposal or specifications, the consulting engineer or buyer should specify that a complete list of spare parts be designated.

General.—Whatever a builder's standard practice may be in regard to any alternative constructions, he is able to manufacture most efficiently and at lowest cost only when following his standard. Deviations from such standards as may be forced by rigid purchase specifications result in higher bids on equipment no better than standard—sometimes not as good as standard.

It is an important point that each builder design his engine to be a harmonious whole. Any requirement which attempts to force him to change some detail in order to conform to a competitive design which has captured the buyer's fancy may upset the harmony of design which, taken as an overall matter, may be quite equal in merit to the favored type. The detailed design of an engine is something on which the builder stakes his entire reputation and business future. It is based upon much experience and continued study by specialists into new materials and construction. The buyer who steps beyond a general specification of capacity, approximate speed, class of duty, weight and space limitations and the like, hampers progress and may secure an inferior offering.

Central Kansas Electric Cooperative Plant, Great Bend, Kansas, with two 3100 kw two-cycle dual fuel engines.

CHAPTER FOUR

Governors and Speed Regulation*

An engine for constant-speed, variable-load duty must be equipped with a governor to adjust the delivery of fuel in response to variations in load in order to maintain the speed substantially constant. Such a governor is actuated by the slight changes in speed which are brought about by change of load.

Governors may be of the relay-powered or centrifugally-powered type. In any application where the engine is used for driving equipment other than generators, the less expensive centrifugally-powered type of governor will often suffice.

The interactions of speed, load and time required for governor operation are described by several terms which should be defined before proceeding further.

Steady-state Operation.—The condition existing when the control system, including both controlled and controlling elements, is operating with all variable quantities within any limits that may have been specified, or if no limits have been specified, are as nearly constant as is practically possible.

Absolute constancy is not implied, but *periodic* deviations are not considered normal to steady-state operation (see Stable Oscillation and Forced Oscillation). Such deviations as do occur in steady-state operation are characterized by their random, aperiodic and variable nature.

Stable Speed Oscillation.—A periodic deviation of constant amplitude from a fixed mean value.

The nature of a system in stable oscillation is such that if by some means the amplitude of the oscillation be either increased or decreased and the disturbing factor subsequently removed, it will return to its original amplitude of oscillation. It results from the fact that for the conditions existing at zero amplitude the system is actually unstable.

Forced Speed Oscillation.—A periodic deviation from a fixed mean value resulting from periodic forces existing in the system.

The oscillations are not of constant amplitude but are usually characterized by a relatively slow modulation, or periodic variation

* A joint AIEE-ASME Committee has prepared "Specifications for the Speed Governing of Internal Combustion Engine-Generator Units" and, concurrently, an ASME Committee is preparing ASME Power Test Code No. 26 entitled "Code on Speed Governing Performance of Internal Combustion Engine-Generator Units." As these DEMA Standard Practices go to press it is uncertain when these two publications will be released. They will be valuable additions to the literature on this subject and their use, when published, is recommended.

in amplitude, of an oscillation of much higher frequency. They differ from stable oscillations not only in their variable amplitude but also in that they do not result from system instability but are forced by regularly recurring variations in load or inaccuracies in governor drive and may be further modified by resonance with various portions of the control system.

Speed Regulation.—Speed regulation is the difference between steady-state no load speed and steady-state full load speed expressed as a percentage of full load speed. This may be expressed as follows: Speed regulation in percent equals

$$\frac{(\text{no load speed} - \text{full load rated speed}) \times 100}{\text{full load rated speed}}$$

Speed Droop.—Speed droop refers only to the characteristics of the governor mechanism without reference to engine operation and has no place in engine specifications. Speed droop is the change in the governor speed based on speed change for full stroke of the servomotor or terminal shaft expressed as a percentage of governor speed when the servomotor or terminal shaft is at the end of its travel in the direction to increase fuel.

Isochronous Governor.—An isochronous governor is one which maintains, or may be adjusted to maintain, zero speed regulation.

Momentary-Overspeed.—Momentary overspeed is the difference between the maximum momentary speed and the final steady-state speed following an instantaneous load decrease expressed as a percentage of the steady-state speed at the time of load change. This is shown in Fig. 3.

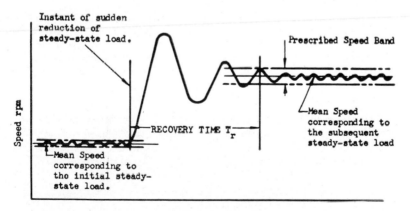

Time in Seconds

Fig. 3. Momentary Speed Conditions with Sudden Reduction of Steady-State Load. For a Sudden Increase the Configuration would be Inverted.

For any load decrease having a value equal to or less than rated power output:

$$S_o = \frac{(n_{max} - n_2) \times 100}{n_1} \%$$

where:

S_o = momentary overspeed
n_1 = steady-state speed at time of load decrease
n_2 = final steady-state speed following load decrease
n_{max} = maximum momentary speed incident to a sudden reduction from one steady-state load to another.

Momentary underspeed is similarly determined.

Recovery Time.—Recovery time is the interval of time required for the speed to return to and remain within a prescribed speed band following an instantaneous change in load. This is shown in Fig. 3.

Stability.—Stability is that property of a dynamic system which causes it to return to a steady-state condition after a disturbance.

Speed Adjustment.—Governors may be supplied with means for changing the speed setting. This may be accomplished either manually at the engine, or electrically by remote control at the switchboard or other point. For variable speed drives, the speed adjustment may permit speeds of one-half normal or less, while for driving electric generators where constant speed is usually required, the adjustment is only sufficient for synchronizing purposes and proper allocation of load between units. In changing speed, the governor still functions although the speed regulation may increase at the lower speeds.

Over-Speed Stop (Sometimes called Over-Speed Trip).— Engines may be supplied with an over-speed stop which automatically shuts off the fuel or otherwise stops the engine in case the engine operates at a speed in excess of some predetermined value. This over-speed stop should be separate from the regular governing mechanism.

Load Division in Parallel Operation.—Division of load between engine driven alternators, provided resonance is not present, is purely a governing function, two separate and distinct, but simultaneous actions of the governor determining the division. The first of these actions depends upon the rapidity of governor response and the second upon governor speed regulation.

The transient division of instantaneous or momentary load changes is determined by the relative rapidity of governor response and the relative Wk^2 of the parallel units. If the load change continues for longer than the recovery time, the load division becomes a function of speed regulation only.

Speed Regulation Characteristics.—As an example of speed regulation characteristics, assume two 300 kw units shown in Fig. 4. The illustration will apply to units of large or small size. The curve for No. 1 unit shows a speed corresponding to 61 cycles at no load and 59 cycles at full load, or a percent speed regulation of

$$\frac{61-59}{59} \times 100\% = 3.39\%$$

The No. 2 unit, by the same method, has a speed regulation of 2.52 percent.

Considering the curve for No. 1 unit alone, it will be seen that the unit is regulated to run at 60-cycle speed when the load is 180 kw. A gradual addition of 30 kw to make the load 210 kw

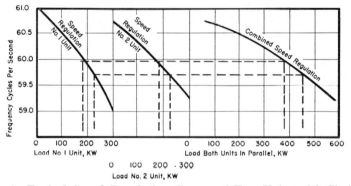

Fig. 4. **Typical Speed Regulation Curves of Two Units with Similar Governors, Operating in Parallel.**

will cause the speed to drop to slightly above that corresponding to 59¾ cycles. A gradual reduction in load to 160 kw will cause an increase to a speed corresponding to slightly less than 60¼ cycles. These changes are shown in the speed-time diagrams in Fig. 5, where the increase and decrease of load are assumed to be instantaneous. The left-hand curve in this figure shows the speed-time relation for an *ideal* governor, with no time lag and no momentary fluctuation in speed other than that due to speed regulation. The right-hand curve illustrates the operation of an actual governor, with momentary speed change.

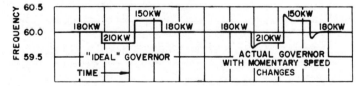

Fig. 5. **Speed-Time Curves of Units with "Ideal" and Typical Governors.**

Paralleling.—Returning to Fig. 4, it will be seen that by adding the abscissae of the two speed regulation curves and plotting the sums on the corresponding ordinates, a speed regulation curve can be constructed for the two units when operating in parallel. Horizontal lines drawn back from this combined curve show the load divisions for any steady load. For instance, a total of 370 kw will be divided into 185 kw for No. 1 unit and 185 kw for No. 2. A total load of 450 kw will be divided into 220 kw for No. 1 and 230 kw for No. 2.

Paralleling of Units with Dissimilar Speed Regulation Curves.—With the advent of relay-powered governors, it has been possible to adjust units to have a minimum speed regulation. An illustration of one such unit in parallel with a unit having a centrifugally-powered governor is shown in Fig. 6. The No. 1 unit shown has a speed regulation of 2/3 of 1 percent, the No. 2 unit a regulation of 3.39 percent. The combined speed regulation curve shows that the normal range of the units in parallel is from 150 kw to 510 kw. At loads below 150 kw the No. 2 unit will not only take all of the load but will actually motorize unit No. 1. For loads over 510 kw, No. 1 unit will be overloaded, No. 2 underloaded.

Shifting the Division of Load.—The steady load division for two or more units operating in parallel can be easily changed by changing the governor adjustment. For instance, Fig. 6 shows 450 kw divided into 250 kw for unit No. 1 and 200 kw for No. 2. If the governor speed setting of unit No. 2 is adjusted to move the speed regulation curve up to the position shown by the broken line, a new (broken) combined curve results. The division of 450 kw is then 175 kw for No. 1 and 275 kw for No. 2.

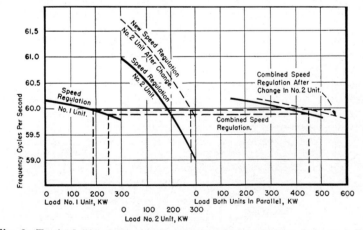

Fig. 6. Typical Speed Regulation Curves of Two Units with Dissimilar Governors, Operating in Parallel.

Incidentally, an adjustment such as indicated by the broken curves has advantages for the units illustrated. It should be noted that the two units can handle 600 kw without overload on either. It is true that 250 kw is the minimum load, below which No. 1 unit will be motorized, but one of the units should be shut down anyway when the load falls to this low point.

When two or more units having the same governing characteristics are operating in parallel, the governors will be equally active in picking up a momentary increase of load for their respective units. Later the operation of a system containing one unit of zero, or nearly zero speed regulation will be discussed. Such a unit must have the capacity to take most of the gradual load fluctuations. It is not necessary that such a unit be large enough to take momentary load increases, because such increases are also distributed among the units with steep speed regulation curves.

Frequency Regulation.—One advantage in operating one unit of nearly flat speed regulation characteristics is the resultant minimum speed variation. The broken combined speed regulation curve of Fig. 6 shows a variation in load from 42 percent to 100 percent, corresponding to a speed variation of 60.2 to 59.8 cycles. The unit with a steep speed regulation becomes a constant, or base load unit, and the unit with the flat speed regulation takes the load variation. In the system represented by the broken curve of Fig. 6, the No. 1 unit, with the flat regulation, has a load variation from full to no load while the variation for the No. 2 unit is only from full to 85 percent load. If the No. 1 unit is adjusted to zero regulation, it will take all of the gradual load changes leaving the No. 2 unit to operate at a constant load corresponding to the speed equal to that of the No. 1 unit.

It is not practical to attempt to adjust more than one unit to zero speed regulation in a system of paralleling units. It would be difficult to set two such units at exactly the same frequency and still more difficult to keep them there. Even if these difficulties did not exist, the steady load division between two such units would be indeterminate.

Uniform Governing.—The preceding paragraphs have discussed regulation of units when equipped with governors giving differing speed regulation. If practicable, it is generally desirable to equip all units in a plant with governors having similar speed regulation characteristics, as by so doing a change in percent of total plant loading will be reflected automatically in a similar change in loading of the individual units.

Effect of Electrical Characteristics on Parallel Operation.—This chapter has dealt with the mechanical considerations of governing, speed regulation and parallel operation. Electrical considerations involved in parallel operation are discussed in Chapter Fourteen.

CHAPTER FIVE

Torsional Vibrations and Critical Speeds

Torsional vibrations occur in any power driven assembly where periodic force impulses are present. At certain speeds these vibrations may become excessive and cause dangerous stresses in the assembly if the periodic force impulses causing these vibrations occur in, or close to resonance with the natural frequency of the system. The period of the natural frequency of torsional vibration is determined by the mass distribution and torsional flexibility between masses.

Any speed at which these periodic forces synchronize with a natural frequency of the system is called a critical speed and may or may not be dangerous, depending upon the forces involved and the arrangement of the vibratory system. Some of the forces which cause these vibrations come from the engine but others may come from the driven equipment especially if it is reciprocating.

It is possible to determine the natural frequencies and the speeds at which serious torsional vibrations may occur if all pertinent data concerning the engine and the driven equipment are known.

In many cases it is possible for the engine manufacturer to change the speeds at which criticals occur by alterations to the connecting members between the engine and driven equipment, or by alterations to the engine itself. These alterations keep harmful criticals away from the operating speed of a constant speed unit. In the case of a variable speed unit these alterations are made to keep the operating range as free of critical speeds as possible. The engine manufacturer will advise the purchaser at which speeds the more significant criticals occur and which speed ranges should be avoided.

Successful operation of the unit depends on proper handling of torsional vibration and critical speed problems. Engine builders have made it their practice to make analyses not only when they furnish the entire equipment but also when a portion of the equipment is furnished by the purchaser, provided the purchaser furnishes the engine manufacturer with the necessary complete and accurate data concerning these parts. When the engine manufacturer furnishes the entire unit he assumes the responsibility of making such changes as are necessary so that in the case of a constant speed unit, no harmful torsional vibration stresses will occur within 10 percent above or below the rated speed. Torsional vibration stresses shall generally be considered harmful if they are more than 5000 psi. For variable speed units the operating range will be kept as free of torsional vibrations as possible and speeds at which harmful stresses occur should be avoided.

In case part of the equipment other than the engine is supplied by the purchaser, the engine manufacturer will assume the same responsibility as to critical speed calculations as if he had furnished the entire assembly, but only to the extent of calculations based upon the accuracy of data supplied by the purchaser with the request for bids.

The driven equipment may consist of a wide variety of apparatus such as generators, exciters, reciprocating pumps, rotary pumps, gears with the necessary connecting shafting, couplings, pulleys, etc., and each element and its relative location has its effect on the location and magnitude of the critical torsional vibrations. It is, therefore, essential that detailed information applying to each driven unit be supplied to the engine manufacturer, such as exact Wk^2 and location of related parts, nature of mounting of these parts on shafting, shafting sizes and material, flexible characteristics of couplings, and weights and particulars of reciprocating parts.

The accuracy of the results of the engine manufacturer's calculations depends upon the accuracy of the information supplied to him and obviously his responsibility is limited accordingly. If alterations are required after the order is placed, due to inaccurate or incomplete information, these should not be made at the expense of the engine manufacturer and he should not be held responsible for delays caused thereby. It may be found necessary to change the purchaser's proposed arrangement, or to modify certain parts of the driven equipment such as shaft sizes, couplings, weight of fly-wheels or counterweights, and in certain cases some form of torsional vibration damping device may be required. In such event the additional expense should be borne by the purchaser.

The purchaser should not alter the arrangement of the driven apparatus, add any additional equipment to, or remove any equipment from a unit without consulting the engine manufacturer as to the effect on the location and magnitude of critical speeds. Any change of this nature might change the location of the critical speeds so as to bring one or more within the operating range of the unit. It is likewise evident that the operating speed range of a unit should not be changed without consulting the engine manufacturer, as the new speed range may include one of the critical speeds or come close enough to it to be dangerous.

Sewage treatment plant at Quincy, Mass., operates five four-cycle gas and dual fuel engines, totalling 2914 hp, on sewage gas.

CHAPTER SIX

Intake and Exhaust Systems and Heat Recovery Apparatus.

The Intake System.—This consists of a duct for leading the combustion air to the engine manifolding from the chosen point of induction, together with such air cleaning, air cooling and air column oscillation damping apparatus as may be required. Most engines perform better with a well designed inlet system than with individual direct inlets to the cylinders, since the velocity head acting toward the engine is maintained without total interruption throughout each cycle.

Since engines, four-cycle and two-cycle, use between two and five cubic feet of air per minute per rated horsepower, the effect of locating the air intake inside the building is readily estimated in the ventilating engineer's terms of "changes of air per minute." Even for power plant buildings in warm regions, the volume of air required for the larger engine installations may be too great to allow proper control of ventilation if taken from inside the building. Hot ground air so taken in during the hot part of the day may cause overheating of the building. In such cases it would be more desirable to depend upon natural ventilation through roof ventilators and to take the intake air from outside the building through a suitable duct.

Figs. 7 and 8 illustrate two methods of installing intake mufflers and filters.

In cold country it is impracticable to heat the full quantity of intake air. Consequently it is almost universal practice to draw air from outside the building, except in the case of relatively small engine installations or where the power plant occupies but a fraction of a large building space which is adequately supplied with heating

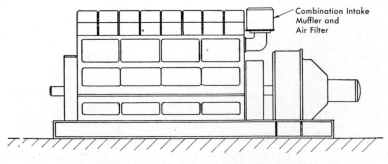

Combination Intake
Muffler and
Air Filter

Fig. 7. Method of Installing Intake Muffler and Air Filter.

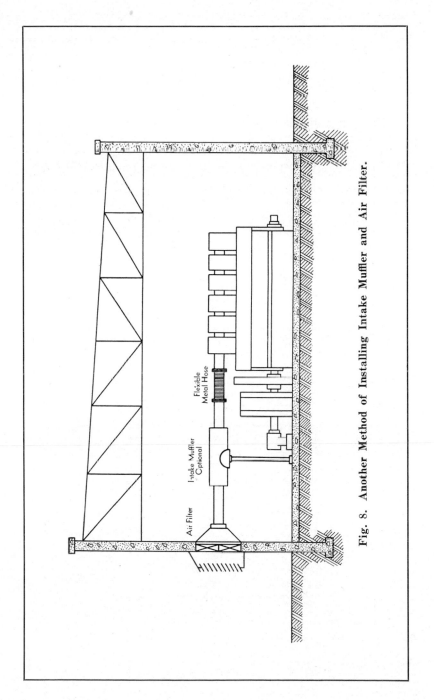

Fig. 8. Another Method of Installing Intake Muffler and Air Filter.

and ventilating equipment for building service in general. To permit quick starts and improve combustion characteristics, when the air is taken from outside the building, particularly in the case of dual fuel or gas-Diesel engines, it is the usual practice to arrange the air intake for blending of the cold air with warm air and not by-pass the air filter. Several methods are practicable and one typical arrangement is shown in Fig. 9.

Intake ducts should be as short and as straight as possible, and any bends should be long radius. It has been common practice in the past to state in engine instruction books that piping for any of the engine services should be of the size indicated by taps or flanges on the engine when runs do not exceed a stated distance. This had its foundation in experience with engines of the past. However, the range of cylinder multiples and speeds offered by engine builders today calls for advice which is better founded on the established theories of vibration in air columns. Therefore, the engine manufacturer should be consulted in designing the intake system. The system should include air intake mufflers where local conditions require low noise levels.

All intakes should be provided with some form of air cleaner whether dry type, oil bath, viscous impingement or electrostatic. While average air pollution varies greatly in different sections, any area is liable to occasional excessive dust conditions and provision should be made for it. Air filters should be placed in a location

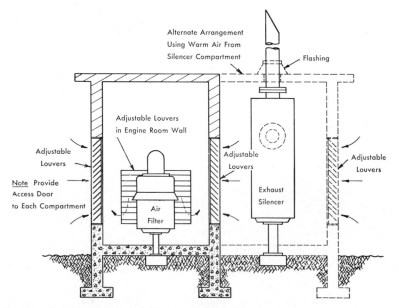

Fig. 9. Typical Air Intake Arrangement for Dual Fuel or Gas-Diesel Engines with Provision for Preheating.

convenient for servicing and with the intake so arranged that ground surface dust or snow will not clog the filter. When the air cleaner is also effective as a muffler, it becomes a more valuable adjunct to a well designed inlet system. The air intake filter should be so located that the combustion air will not be contaminated or heated by the exhaust, or by hot air from a radiator, evaporative condenser or other type cooler.

Where turbo-blower superchargers are used they are sometimes fitted with an inlet screen and acoustic silencer by the maker. If remote intakes are required, special advice should be secured from the engine builder.

The mass of inlet pipe should be isolated from the engine by use of suitable flexible connection, where necessary.

Light weight steel pipe and fittings may be used for the intake system. Flanged bent pipe with long radius turns make a sightly and efficient job, readily available since pipe bending and welding contractors are found in most cities. Concrete or masonry ducts, if used, should be thoroughly dust-proofed and care taken to keep out contamination.

The Exhaust System.—Exhaust ducts for manifolded multiple-cylinder two-cycle and four-cycle engines are designed by the principles discussed in the section on the intake system. This design must be carefully worked out by the engine builder for the particular type of engine involved and should include mufflers, if necessary, to reduce exhaust noise to meet local requirements.

The muffler design should employ acoustic principles rather than throttling. The total allowable resistance, subject to the inaccuracies of manometer measurements of an oscillating pressure, will be given by the engine builder. Muffler designers are well acquainted with the requirements of different engine types, sizes and speeds and can be relied upon to recommend mufflers to effectively reduce exhaust noises without impairing engine efficiency.

Engines equipped with exhaust gas driven turbochargers can sometimes be used without exhaust silencers because of the silencing effect of the turbocharger. Exhaust silencers are required if the installation is in a critical area or if a spark arresting feature is necessary.

The exhaust system should never be rigidly secured to the engine. Expansion and vibration isolation should be assured by use of flexible connections. Exhaust pipes should be as short and as straight as possible and any bends should be long radius. Welded, flanged, and bent pipe are preferable to standard pipe fittings. Suitable and accessible clean-out pockets and covers should be provided where required.

Masonry is not considered desirable for exhaust stacks, ducts or chambers. This is particularly true of brickwork or tile. Such structures generally have poor resistance against vibration resulting from exhaust pulsations. Under no circumstances should they be used.

In the case of an existing stack where there is the slightest doubt regarding its suitability, the engine manufacturer should be consulted. Regardless of the type of stack used, proper provision for expansion of connecting piping must be made.

It is not desirable to combine the exhaust of two or more engines. Each should have its own exhaust line to the atmosphere, with the outlet extending several feet above an adjacent wall or roof.

Fig. 10 illustrates a method of installing exhaust mufflers. Caution should be exercised in the installation of exhaust stacks or ducts so that they will not be near or in contact with combustible material when passing through a wall or roof. Ample clearance should be provided and insulating sleeves used where necessary.

Exhaust pyrometers are recommended as a desirable accessory. When properly used, they provide a simple and reliable means of checking load balances between cylinders.

Waste Heat Recovery.—Projects for utilizing jacket water and exhaust heat should be scrutinized carefully, apart from the fundamental power plant, for potential recovery on the investment and also for their influence on the service cost and reliability of the whole plant.

The table shows typical examples of heat disposition in a Diesel engine at three-quarters to full load:

Fuel consumption, Btu/bhp-hr	7366
Useful work, Btu/bhp-hr	2544
Loss in radiation, etc., Btu/bhp-hr	370
To cooling water, Btu/bhp-hr	2194
To exhaust, Btu/bhp-hr	2258

This balance will vary between cooling water and exhaust for different classes of engines, depending upon the degree of cooling applied to pistons, exhaust manifolding and intake air. For any close engineering analysis, exact figures should be procured for individual cases.

For approximate calculations, the quantities of heat rejected to engine cooling water and exhaust are equal and each is equivalent to about 2.4 gallons of water per actual hp-hr raised through 100 F. but not all is recoverable for various reasons.

The most efficient use of waste heat is through the direct use of jacket water with heat supplemented by the exhaust. This is desirable only in closed systems such as hot water heating, since jacket water usually is selected or treated water, and cannot be run to waste.

When it is desired to make steam, an adverse condition enters. Assuming that each pound of water leaving the jacket picks up 100 Btu, it is necessary to add about 1000 Btu to turn this same

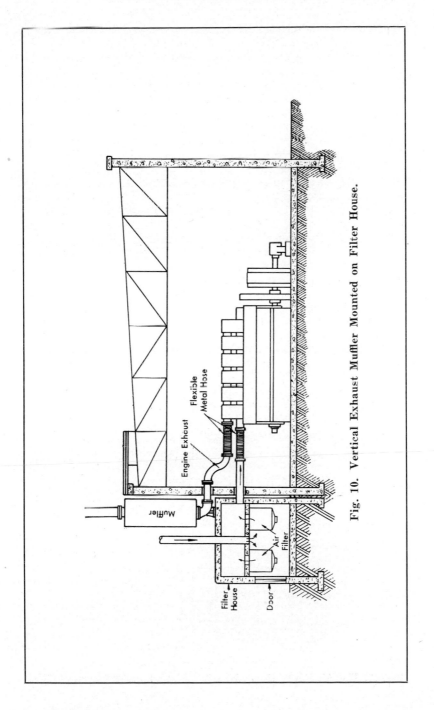

Fig. 10. Vertical Exhaust Muffler Mounted on Filter House.

pound of water into steam. Thus only a fraction of the jacket water, primary or secondary, may be used as boiler feed and the remaining jacket water heat must be dissipated elsewhere.

The amount of exhaust heat that may be recovered is reduced to 60 percent or 70 percent of the total, mainly by the necessity of maintaining a final exhaust temperature of at least 250 F to avoid precipitation of water in the system and resulting acid formation and rapid corrosion, which would occur if the exhaust gas were to be cooled below the dew point.

Every plant of this sort is an engineering project if high recovery is essential and should be so handled, as it cannot be within the scope of this chapter to give specific performance data for the wide range of conditions possible with the increasing use of waste heat recovery apparatus. Certainly all power plant heating requirements should be met by use of waste heat, although full auxiliary heating apparatus should be provided in cold regions as a factor of safety.

In moderate climates a very satisfactory way of utilizing exhaust heat is to air-jacket the exhaust pipe uptake, using it for a chimney in the summer and reversing the flow by use of a fan when heat is required (See Fig. 11.)

For more complete utilization of waste heat recovery from engine exhaust, there are several types of exhaust heat boilers of fire tube, water tube and thimble tube construction, as well as finned-wall heat recovery silencers having the acoustic features of conventional

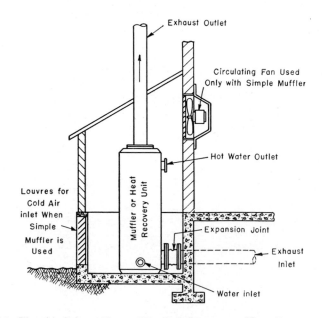

Fig. 11. Hot Air Power House Heating System or Heat Recovery Unit.

mufflers. All of these are capable of producing considerable quantities of hot water and low pressure steam from the larger engine installation, when the load factor is 50 percent or greater. The present limit for steam pressure is about 100 psi but the efficiency is greater and the installation simplified if working pressures are 15 psi or less.

All of the exhaust heat boilers are known to have some muffling properties, but it is not general practice to consider them as mufflers, except the heat recovery silencer type, because they may not be adequate in this respect for many localities and also because not all of them may be operated dry with safety. Some exhaust heat boilers are designed to operate dry without damage if exhaust temperatures do not exceed a certain value, approximately 800 F. In some cases conditions may require a regular muffler with blank flanged connections or a three-way swing or butterfly valve in the piping so that the exhaust can be made to flow through either the boiler or the muffler as desired.

Individual boilers are recommended for each engine.

All exhaust heat boilers should come equipped from the manufacturer with standard "boiler trim," namely, pressure gage, water gage, try cocks, safety valve and surface and bottom blow-off valves. The boiler manufacturer should be informed as to:

1. Engine specifications, i.e., make, model, cycle, bore and stroke, number of cylinders, horsepower, rpm, average load, weight of exhaust gas in pounds per hour, exhaust temperature range, and permissible exhaust back pressure.

2. Temperature and quality of available feed water.

3. Final temperature of water or pressure of steam required.

4. Quantity of hot water or steam required per hour.

5. Location (with respect to engine).

6. Type of automatic heat recovery controls required.

7. Type of condensate return system required.

8. Whether boiler is to be insulated and, if so, what type.

9. What boiler accessories are required in addition to the standard "boiler trim."

10. What state laws, local ordinances or regulations govern construction and installation of such pressure vessels, in addition to ASME Code requirements, and what permits are required.

Fig. 11 illustrates a simplified method of installing exhaust heat boilers or exhaust heat recovery silencers. Specific diagrams and instructions are necessary and are obtained from the manufacturer.

CHAPTER SEVEN

Starting Systems

Various methods are used to bring engines up to the required speed for starting. Compressed air is usually employed and in such cases opening of air starting valves automatically admits compressed air to the power cylinders in predetermined sequence. Certain engines of small bore and stroke may be hand-cranked, usually in the single cylinder models. Medium and large size, high-speed engines may be brought up to starting speed by various other methods such as an attached electric motor, air motor, or gasoline engine. Engines driving direct current generators are sometimes cranked by motorizing the generator from a separate source of direct current.

Air Starting.—This system is the one most used in low and medium speed engine service. Some of the older engines operate on various starting air pressures from 250 to 1000 psi, but most engine builders now design their engines for starting air pressures of 250 to 350 psi.

The starting air system consists of an air compressor with a driving motor or engine, air storage tanks, pressure gages, relief valves, piping to the engine or engines, and control valves located on or near the engines. A typical starting air system is shown in Fig. 12. A compressor raises air to the pressure used in starting, and is protected by spring-loaded safety valves. The compressed air is stored in the air tanks or receivers which are equipped with shut-off valves, pressure gages, relief valves and with drain valves to remove condensed water vapor. Air for starting is obtained directly from the tanks without the use of reducing valves.

Many plants rely on a motor driven compressor, usually equipped with an automatic stop and start control by a pressure switch. Some compressors are gasoline engine driven or a combination of gasoline engine and motor drive. Such units have an advantage in that starting air pressure can be restored when no other source of power is available. The compressor is usually two-stage and may be either air or water cooled depending on the size and duty.

Compressor Capacity.—The capacity and number of compressors are determined by the size and number of engines in the plant, operating conditions, and the contract requirements. The minimum compressor capacity should be sufficient to replenish in one hour the starting air supply for the largest unit after such supply has been reduced to the minimum pressure necessary to start the engine.

Air Storage Capacity.—The tank capacity will depend on the starting pressure, the number of starts required without recharging

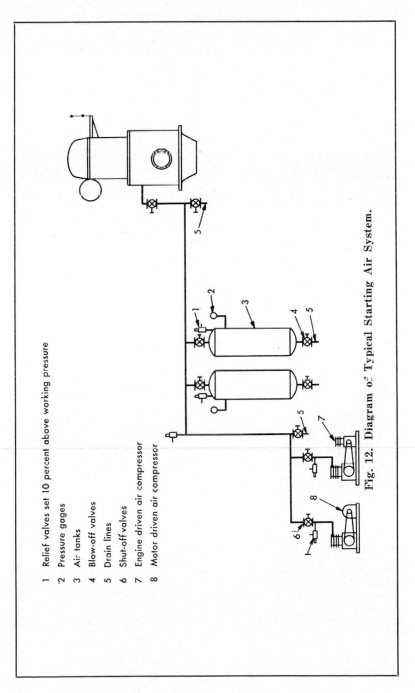

1 Relief valves set 10 percent above working pressure
2 Pressure gages
3 Air tanks
4 Blow-off valves
5 Drain lines
6 Shut-off valves
7 Engine driven air compressor
8 Motor driven air compressor

Fig. 12. Diagram of Typical Starting Air System.

the tanks, the number of engines in the plant and the requirements of the largest engine. At least two tanks should be supplied in each plant. The engine builder should be consulted for his recommendations.

Air Tank Construction.—Starting air tanks should be made in accordance with the Rules of Construction of Unfired Pressure Vessels, American Society of Mechanical Engineers* Boiler Construction Code. If there are state, local or insurance regulations which apply to such tanks, the buyer should furnish the engine builder with full details to assure compliance with such rules.

Installation of Air Tanks.—Air tanks should be located between the air compressors and the engine, as shown in Fig. 12 and in such a manner that all external surfaces can be inspected, cleaned and painted when necessary without removing the tanks from their locations. Tanks should be located as close to engines as is practicable in order to reduce pressure losses between tanks and engines. Installation of tanks and their fittings should also meet state, local and insurance regulations. Tanks should be installed in a reasonably dry place and in such manner that the openings for internal inspection (if any) are accessible without removing the tanks. Positions may be vertical or horizontal, with the outlet to the engine at or near the top. Vertical tanks should be mounted on supporting rings, and horizontal tanks on suitable saddles or wall brackets. Air tanks should be installed with conveniently located drains for removal of condensed moisture at frequent intervals.

Installation of Air Compressors.—Compressor air intakes should be located to receive cool and clean air. Air intake filters and mufflers are sometimes desirable in maintaining internal compressor cleanliness and eliminating objectionable noise. It is important to note that a relief valve must be placed in the pipe between the compressor discharge and the compressor shut-off valve, as shown in Fig. 12.

Air Tank Fittings.—Each air tank should be equipped with the following fittings (See Fig. 12):
>   One main stop or shut-off valve.
>   One pressure gage.
>   One spring-loaded relief valve.
>   One drain or bottom blow-off valve.

Piping, Valves and Fittings.—Air system pipe sizes should not be smaller than recommended by the engine builder. The type of piping, valves and fittings should be suitable for the starting air pressure. Unions, either screwed or flanged, depending upon size and pressure requirements, should be located to facilitate the dismantling of equipment or fittings without losing tank pressure.

---

* 29 W. 39th St., New York 18, N. Y. See footnote page 168.

Drain valves should be conveniently located and placed wherever necessary to drain the entire system. If they must be located at the end of a length of pipe to be accessible, another valve should be placed immediately adjacent to the tank so that it can be shut off to prevent loss of air pressure in the event of damage to the drain line.

Pipe supports or clamps should be provided wherever necessary to support the piping and reduce vibration to a minimum. The tank manifold should be made up in such a manner that the spring of the piping provides some flexibility.

Electric Starting.—In some direct current engine electric applications, each main generator may be equipped with special starting windings to enable it to crank the engine to which it is connected. The generator is supplied with direct current from a storage battery or other source of direct current. In some systems, the electrical circuit is arranged so that the starting winding of the generator is only in the circuit during the cranking period and accordingly a cut out, as well as a remote control switch, is required.

Another method used where engine driven direct current generators are operated in parallel with other units, or an external direct current line, utilizes the main generator as a motor. Closing the main circuit breaker energizes the machine and brings it up to speed, after which fuel is admitted to the cylinders and the engine is brought into operation.

Automatic Starting.—It is generally possible to start an engine from a remote control position or automatically from some control pilot device sensitive to the requirements for starting. Such starting is sometimes mandatory in the case of standby electrical service and various pumping applications. In such cases the engine manufacturer should be informed of these requirements so he can incorporate necessary mechanical or electrical equipment required to adapt his engine to this condition, and for his recommendation as to specialty manufacturers for other equipment not normally manufactured by him but necessary for the overall operation.

Trico Utilities Plant at Tucson, Arizona, with five four-cycle Diesel 1000 kw generating sets.

CHAPTER EIGHT

Cooling Water Systems

When fuel is burned in an engine, part of the heat energy is transformed into useful work. Some passes out with the exhaust gases, some is lost by radiation, and the remainder is absorbed by the cooling water and lubricating oil. The cooling water system consists of equipment required to dissipate heat of the engine absorbed by water circulated through the engine and through the lubricating oil cooler, if the latter is used.

While heat exchangers are used for either water or oil cooling, the usual practice, and the one followed in this text, is to consider the term "heat exchanger" as applying to jacket water cooling.

Heat Balance.—The amount of heat absorbed by the cooling water varies with the type of engine, design of cylinders, exhaust manifold, pistons, lubricating oil system and any other equipment which may be cooled directly or indirectly by the circulating water.

The variation in cooling requirements is such that the final design of the cooling system should not be made until the specific size, type and make of engines are selected.

When engines are equipped with air pre-coolers or air after-coolers or both, a suitable supply of cooling water at temperatures specified by the engine builder is necessary in addition to that normally required for the engine jackets and lubricating oil coolers.

The temperature and quantity of water required will vary with the size, type and make of engine and with maximum ambient temperatures at the location of installation.

It is desirable to keep engine jacket inlet and outlet temperature differential of the circulating water at a minimum, preferably less than 15 to 20 F.

Consideration for Cooling Systems.—The cooling water system that provides for best engine performance is designed and selected to maintain a constant jacket water outlet temperature and lubricating oil temperature, both within the limits recommended by the engine manufacturer. These requirements must be met for varying load conditions under atmospheric variations prevailing at the location of the installation.

Seasonal temperature variations may cause freezing of water and congealing of lubricating oil. Regardless of the cooling system used, provision should be made to prevent damage from these conditions.

The system should be designed so that all of the water flows through the engine at all times. The water flow should never be throttled to raise the outlet temperature. To maintain a uniform heat transfer and a high efficiency of cooling through the engine jackets, only soft water or treated water should be circulated through the engine. The character of the water should be such that there will be no deposit in the water spaces. It should also be free of corrosive properties, and a pH value between 8.0 and 9.5 should be maintained for minimum corrosion. A competent water chemist should be consulted for recommendations on the treatment of water to prevent corrosion and the forming of scale.

The system should be vented so that water spaces will be completely filled at all times.

In designing a cooling water system and in selecting equipment for it, many factors must be considered, such as the following:

1. Water supply. What are the hardness and corrosive characteristics? Is the supply ample or limited? Is it sea water, river water, lake water, or well water? Is it brackish?

2. Atmospheric conditions. What are maximum and minimum wet and dry bulb temperatures? What is the average wind velocity and its direction? Is the locality subject to dust storms?

3. Space available. Can all of the equipment be installed indoors, or must part of it be installed outdoors? In either case, how much space is available to accommodate the cooling equipment?

4. Heat recovery. Is it desirable to recover heat from the jacket water for space heating or for other uses around or near the plant?

Equipment to dissipate heat from jacket water has become highly specialized. There are many reliable manufacturers capable of recommending suitable equipment after conditions of service are known. The amount of heat to be removed from the engine jackets and from the lubricating oil and the limiting water temperatures should always be obtained from the engine manufacturer. It is then the cooling equipment manufacturer's entire responsibility to supply adequate heat exchange equipment to dissipate the specified amount of heat for actual service conditions during the life of the equipment.

Details of various types of cooling systems are illustrated by arrangement diagrams throughout this chapter. Final details and the manner of arrangement of equipment may vary according to different engine manufacturer's preferences. For example, one manufacturer may prefer the circulating water pump with suction from the engine, and another may prefer the circulating water pump with discharge to the engine.

Heat exchangers for jacket water and lubricating oil should be installed with outlet connections on top unless suitable vents are provided.

Figs. 13, 14, 15 and 16 are schematic diagrams of arrangements of soft and raw water circuits that may be used in the various

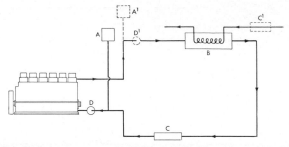

Fig. 13. General Arrangement of Engine Cooling System for Moderate
Temperatures.

A — Surge or Expansion Tank
A[1]— Alternate Location of Expansion Tank
B — Heat Exchanger
C — Lubricating Oil Cooler
C[1]— Alternate Location of Lubricating Oil Cooler
D — Jacket Water Pump
D[1]— Alternate Location of Jacket Water Pump

Notes: 1. Heat exchanger outlet temperature to suit lubricating oil
cooler.
2. A by-pass (not shown) to control temperatures may be used
either on heat exchanger or on lubricating oil cooler.

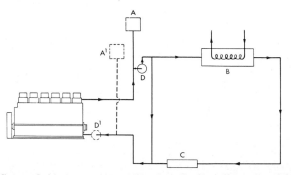

Fig. 14. General Arrangement of Engine Cooling System, with Part of
Water By-Passing Heat Exchanger, Permitting Higher Temperature
to Engine and Lower Temperature to Lubricating Oil Cooler.

A — Surge or Expansion Tank
A[1]— Alternate Location of Expansion Tank
B — Heat Exchanger
C — Lubricating Oil Cooler
D — Jacket Water Pump
D[1]— Alternate Location of Jacket Water Pump

Note: By-pass to control temperatures.

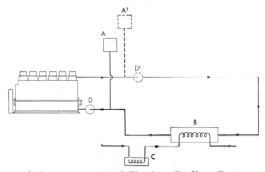

Fig. 15. General Arrangement of Engine Cooling System, with Lubricating Oil Cooler in Separate Circuit, Permitting Higher Water Temperature to Engine.

A — Surge or Expansion Tank
A¹— Alternate Location of Expansion Tank
B — Heat Exchanger
C — Lubricating Oil Cooler
D — Jacket Water Pump
D¹— Alternate Location of Jacket Water Pump

Note: A by-pass (not shown) to control temperatures may be used either on heat exchanger or on lubricating oil cooler.

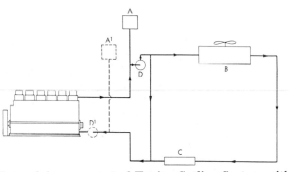

Fig. 16. General Arrangement of Engine Cooling System, with Part of Water By-Passing Dry Type Heat Exchanger (Radiator), Permitting Higher Temperature to Engine and Lower Temperature to Lubricating Oil Cooler.

A — Surge or Expansion Tank
A¹— Alternate Location of Expansion Tank
B — Dry Heat Exchanger
C — Lubricating Oil Cooler
D — Jacket Water Pump
D¹— Alternate Location of Jacket Water Pump

Note: By-pass or air control to control water temperatures.

types of closed cooling systems described in some detail on the following pages. Many variations of these systems are possible.

There are two general types of cooling systems known as the "Open System" and the "Closed System," with many variations of each.

Open Cooling System.—The open cooling system is one in which the water under pressure flows through the engine jackets, and is wasted or recirculated through a cooling tower. The recooling of water by cooling tower or spray pond is a process dependent upon evaporation. Continued evaporation and addition of makeup water increases the concentration of either hardness or impurities and causes the water to become increasingly objectionable for use in the engine jackets.

The accumulation of scale forming materials will not remain in solution but will be deposited in the jackets of the engine, retarding the transfer of the heat from the metal walls to the cooling water. This is detrimental to the engine. Therefore the open cooling system is generally not recommended.

Closed Cooling System.—The closed cooling system is recommended. The arrangement may consist of either one or two complete systems of circulating water. If, for example, a radiator is used with air as the cooling medium, a single system is used with water flowing through the engine jackets and then through the radiator.

Other examples are the shell and tube heat exchanger, a cooling tower with heat exchanger, and an evaporative cooler. These types have two water circulating systems, the jacket water and the raw water.

Jacket water outlet temperature and the rate of flow of water must be as specified by the engine builder. Raw water temperatures, rate of flow and heat load govern the requirements of the cooling apparatus.

Closed Cooling System With Raw Water

1. With Cooling Tower.—The arrangement shown in Fig. 17 illustrates a closed cooling system which includes an induced draft tower with a heat exchanger in the base. The raw water is recirculated in the tower and over the heat exchanger.

Jacket water is pumped through the system by a motor or engine driven pump. Water circulates through the engine and then through the heat exchanger where the heat is dissipated through the raw water. When an oil cooler is used it may be placed in either the raw water circuit or in the jacket water circuit, depending upon the practice of the engine manufacturer. An expansion tank or a standpipe provides for expansion of the jacket water. Either may be equipped with a float control valve to supply makeup water and to replenish water lost through the pump packing in the jacket water circuit.

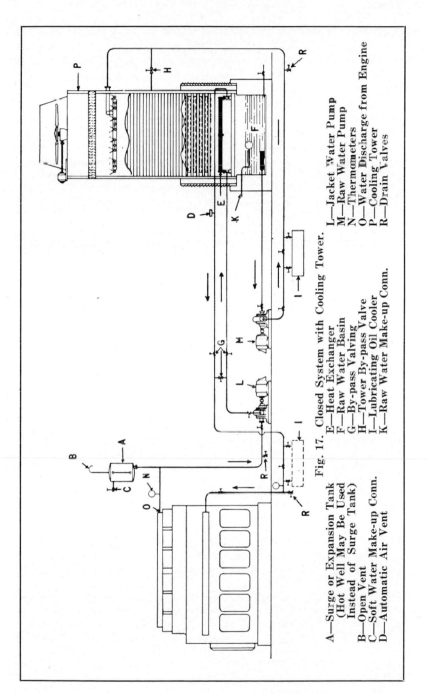

Fig. 17. Closed System with Cooling Tower.

A—Surge or Expansion Tank
  (Hot Well May Be Used
  Instead of Surge Tank)
B—Open Vent
C—Soft Water Make-up Conn.
D—Automatic Air Vent

E—Heat Exchanger
F—Raw Water Basin
G—By-pass Valving
H—Tower By-pass Valve
I—Lubricating Oil Cooler
K—Raw Water Make-up Conn.

L—Jacket Water Pump
M—Raw Water Pump
N—Thermometers
O—Water Discharge from Engine
P—Cooling Tower
R—Drain Valves

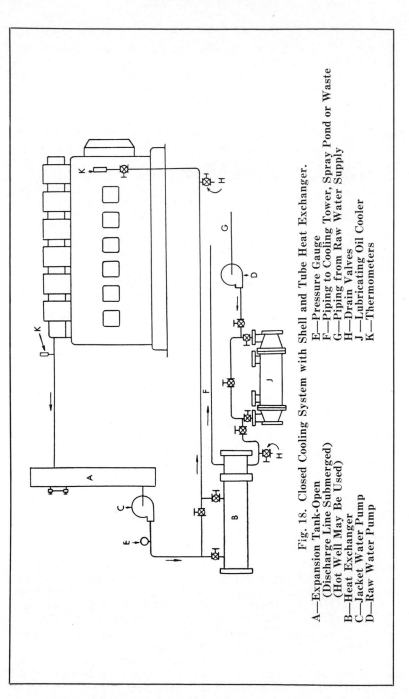

Fig. 18. Closed Cooling System with Shell and Tube Heat Exchanger.

A—Expansion Tank-Open
    (Discharge Line Submerged)
    (Hot Well May Be Used)
B—Heat Exchanger
C—Jacket Water Pump
D—Raw Water Pump
E—Pressure Gauge
F—Piping to Cooling Tower, Spray Pond or Waste
G—Piping from Raw Water Supply
H—Drain Valves
J—Lubricating Oil Cooler
K—Thermometers

The cooling tower may be one of two types, the atmospheric or the induced draft type. The atmospheric type depends upon natural draft or air movement causing evaporation sufficient to remove heat from the raw water. An induced draft tower utilizes a fan to create the necessary air movement to cause sufficient evaporation for required cooling.

In certain localities it may be advantageous to install the heat exchanger inside the building. In this case a shell and tube type heat exchanger is used. The raw water is then circulated over the tower and through the heat exchanger.

Instead of the cooling tower a spray pond may be installed if space is available, and if makeup water is plentiful. To prevent loss of water from drift and help reduce makeup requirements, a louvred fence should be built around the spray pond.

2. With Shell and Tube Type Heat Exchangers.—The shell and tube type heat exchanger system is illustrated in Fig. 18. The heat exchanger is located inside the building. Raw water can be taken from any suitable body of water nearby or from a cooling tower similar to the one illustrated in Fig. 17, but without the atmospheric heat exchanger or coils in the base of the tower. When this system is used it is well to provide a by-pass for the water around the lubricating oil cooler for the purpose of maintaining proper oil temperatures. While Fig. 18 shows the lubricating oil cooler located in the raw water circuit ahead of the jacket water heat exchanger, it may be located in the jacket water circuit as shown in Fig. 17.

Closed Cooling System with Radiator.—One arrangement of a cooling system with a radiator is illustrated by Fig. 19. This illustration also shows how heat extracted from the cooling water may be used for space heating with duct work installed to carry heat away from the radiator. Another method of extracting heat from jacket water for space heating is the utilization of small space heaters. Fig. 19 also shows an installation of space heaters with a radiator.

In connection with lubricating oil cooling, one of four general types of radiator systems may be used:

1. Direct cooling of the oil in a separate part of the radiator.

2. Cooling of two separate streams of water in separate sections of the radiator. In one section the jacket water stream is at a comparatively high temperature. In the other section, the water is cooled to a lower temperature and circulated through the lubricating oil cooler by a separate water pump.

3. A portion of the jacket water is circulated through the radiator and is cooled from the temperature at which it leaves the engine to a comparatively low temperature. The cool water from the radiator is then passed through the lubricating oil cooler before it blends with the remainder of the jacket water which by-passed the radiator and lubricating oil cooler.

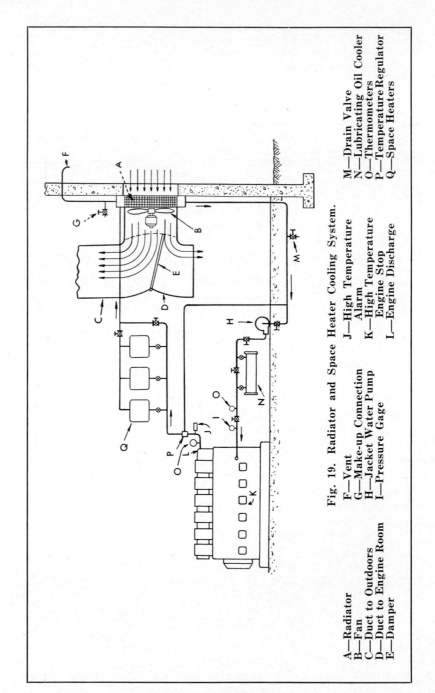

Fig. 19. Radiator and Space Heater Cooling System.

A—Radiator
B—Fan
C—Duct to Outdoors
D—Duct to Engine Room
E—Damper

F—Vent
G—Make-up Connection
H—Jacket Water Pump
I—Pressure Gage

J—High Temperature
    Alarm
K—High Temperature
    Engine Stop
L—Engine Discharge

M—Drain Valve
N—Lubricating Oil Cooler
O—Thermometers
P—Temperature Regulator
Q—Space Heaters

4. All of the jacket water flows through the radiator and then through the lubricating oil cooler. Temperature is controlled by adjustment of radiator louvres or fan speed.

Radiators installed at ground level must be located with the inlet and outlet ducts arranged so that:

1. Air does not recirculate through the radiator under normal conditions.

2. Hot air from radiator does not exhaust into engine air intake.

3. Wind direction and velocity will not counteract the normal air circulation from the fan.

Either a surge tank or a standpipe must be installed in the cooling water circuit to provide for venting, for water expansion, and for introducing makeup water.

Closed Cooling System with Evaporative Cooler.—A cooling system with an evaporative cooler, in principle of operation, is similar to the induced draft cooling tower with a heat exchanger in or near the base of the tower. Evaporative coolers are compact and require a limited space. The raw water circuit with water pumps, coils, spray nozzles and interconnecting piping is integral with the unit and is equipped so that there is practically no raw water fluid loss except by evaporation. Because the raw water circuit is self contained, the amount of external piping required for this system is the same as that required for a radiator of equal capacity.

An arrangement of a closed cooling system with evaporative cooler is shown in Fig. 20.

A small pump usually located in the base of the cooler circulates raw water and sprays it over the coils or heat exchanger.

A fan in the top of the cooler creates an induced draft so that air entering the bottom passes through the water spray and returns to the atmosphere.

The jacket water circulates through the coils or heat exchanger in the same manner as in any other system. Evaporative coolers are sometimes equipped with lubricating oil sections.

To maintain high efficiency of evaporative coolers, initial and makeup water should be treated to prevent accumulation of scale and of algae on the coils of the heat exchanger.

Because of the different provisions that may be made for intake and outlet air ducts, especially for coolers installed indoors, it is not the practice of the cooler manufacturer to supply inlet and outlet air ducts, but their layout should have his approval. The discharge air contains considerable moisture and therefore the discharge duct should be arranged so the air will not blow on the engine air intake filter or other objects that might be damaged by moisture or ice accumulation. Provision for installation of air ducts must be made by the buyer.

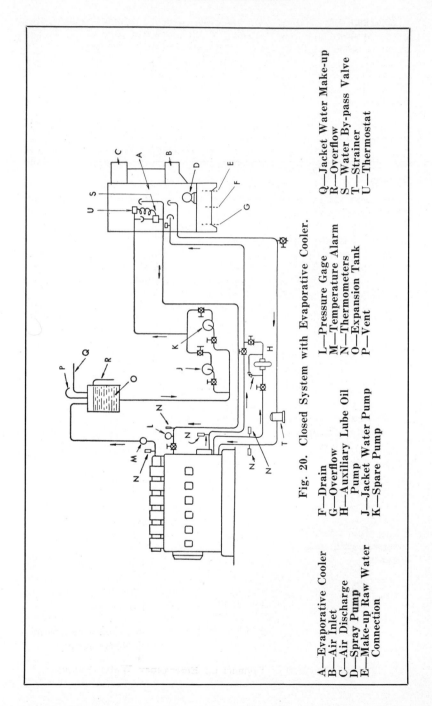

Fig. 20. Closed System with Evaporative Cooler.

A—Evaporative Cooler
B—Air Inlet
C—Air Discharge
D—Spray Pump
E—Make-up Raw Water
    Connection

F—Drain
G—Overflow
H—Auxiliary Lube Oil
    Pump
J—Jacket Water Pump
K—Spare Pump

L—Pressure Gage
M—Temperature Alarm
N—Thermometers
O—Expansion Tank
P—Vent

Q—Jacket Water Make-up
R—Overflow
S—Water By-pass Valve
T—Strainer
U—Thermostat

Emergency Water Connection.—Fig. 21 illustrates an emergency system whereby the flow of jacket water is assured in the event of a failure in the regular system when the required pressure of the water drops below a predetermined point. This system can be used where city water or other source can be assured at all times. It is important that this water should enter the system at a point where it will be tempered before going into the engine jackets.

Alarms.—It is desirable on all cooling systems to incorporate alarms so that the operating personnel are notified when the temperatures or pressures vary from a predetermined point. There are various types of alarm systems which include audible or visible signals.

Shutdown Devices.—In addition to the alarms, it is sometimes desirable to have automatic engine shutdown devices which will operate when the cooling system temperatures or pressures have reached a predetermined point.

The temperatures or pressures for the shutdown devices should be set slightly beyond the predetermined point for the alarms, yet not in excess of the safe operating temperatures or pressures of the engine for a short period of time.

Thermostatic Controls.—Automatic thermostatic controls are quite extensively used where it is not desired to adjust the flow of jacket or raw water manually. These thermostats can be applied in

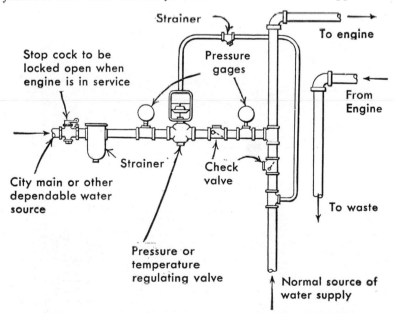

Fig. 21. Method of Connecting Emergency Water Supply.

a system so that the engine is always operating with a fixed outlet temperature from the engine or the lubricating oil cooler, without reducing volume flow through the engine.

The cooling water should be brought to the normal operating temperature before the engine is started, or as soon thereafter as possible. This is done by utilizing heat from another source or by by-passing the cooling tower, radiator, or evaporative cooler until such time as normal temperature is reached.

Multiple Unit Plants.—Where multiple unit plants are being considered, it may be advisable to install standby motor driven pumps with inter-connecting pipe. In a large installation this additional cost is usually justified.

In certain applications it may be desirable to have a separate jacket water system complete for each unit. This provides for greater flexibility and is particularly advantageous if various makes of engines are used requiring different operating temperatures.

Piping and Fittings.—All piping systems should be designed to be simple and fool-proof with all valves in convenient locations for operation. Thermometers should be located for easy observation, and fittings that may require maintenance should be in accessible locations.

The piping should be liberal in size and long sweep fittings should be utilized where possible to reduce friction losses.

World's largest self-powered pumping plant containing six 10-cylinder opposed piston Diesel engines chain driven to drainage pumps of the Central and Southern Florida Flood Control District. This is Station 5A at Belle Glade, Florida, which has a total capacity of over three billion gallons per day.

CHAPTER NINE

Lubricating Oil Systems

Details of the lubricating oil system for each engine design are decided on by the engine manufacturer only after full consideration of the various design features and the resulting lubrication requirements. For many of the smaller units, all or most of the system will be built-in or attached to the engine itself. As the engine size increases, the exterior and accessory equipment items become larger and they may therefore be mounted separately for the sake of convenience and accessibility.

The complete lubricating oil system might be classified in two main sections. The first section consists of the oil piping within and on the engine, the oil sump when part of the engine crankcase, any built-in oil strainers or filters, and the built-in engine-driven oil circulating pumps. Some engines are fitted with mechanical lubricators which furnish oil for cylinder and piston lubrication, and these are included in this grouping.

The second section consists of storage tanks, oil-purification equipment, oil-cooling equipment, indicating or recording instruments, safety or protective devices, control valves, the necessary connecting piping and main or auxiliary pumps and sumps if not part of the engine. Each element of the system must be selected to coordinate with all the other elements.

For engine types where the lubricating oil is used for piston cooling, the elements must be selected to include the requirements of piston cooling as well as engine lubrication.

Oil Storage.—This is usually selected with reference to size and location to suit the requirements of the engine user. In general, it is desirable to be able to remove the contents of the entire system of at least the largest unit at one time and store it without waste.

Iron and steel containers are preferable because some metals such as copper and zinc promote oxidation. For this reason galvanized containers or those made with alloys of copper should not be used for storing oil.

Particular precaution should be taken to eliminate water, dirt, dust or other contaminants from the oil during storage.

Circulating Pumps.—Many engines are fitted with one or more built-in engine-driven lubricating oil pumps for various services. The pumps operate, of course, whenever the engine runs and are of the positive displacement type.

A number of large engine installations are often arranged to have independent electric motor-driven main lubricating oil pumps, which may also serve as prelubrication and after-cooling pumps.

Lubricating oil pumps are always designed to have a capacity greater than required for lubricating and cooling purposes, in order to compensate for the adverse effects of pump wear and the increased demand as engine bearings wear. A pressure relief valve is usually installed to hold a constant pressure by permitting any excess oil to by-pass to the pump suction or to the engine sump.

Auxiliary Lubricating Oil Pump.—An independent motor-driven pump is a useful accessory. If the engine requires more than one pump, say for a piston-cooling system separate from the principal circuit for bearing lubrication, a second auxiliary pump is usually installed; or, in special circumstances, a single unit is used having a total capacity equal to the sum of the requirements of the piston-cooling and circulating systems.

When an auxiliary unit is furnished it may be used before and during start-up to fill all pipe lines and to put the oil in circulation before motion actually occurs. A hand-driven pump is occasionally used to build up the oil supply prior to starting the engine.

Similarly, the auxiliary pumps may be used upon engine shut-down and immediately afterward, as instructed by the engine builder, both to insure a full supply of lubricant until the engine comes completely to rest and to carry away any residual heat.

Oil Purification Equipment.—A wide range of lubricating oil purification equipment is available. Selection must be carefully made, with full consideration of the lubricating needs of the engines and of the type of lubricating oil to be used. The nature of the latter, particularly if it contains additives, has an important bearing on the selection of oil purification methods and equipment. Connections to purification equipment should always be from the lowest point in the crankcase or settling tank to prevent accumulation of water or sludge.

The first requirement in oil treatment is the removal of the larger particles of solid foreign matter which may enter the system. Nothing solid should be permitted to circulate with the oil that is thicker than the oil film in the bearings. Most engines are fitted with strainers for this purpose and it is customary to provide sufficient straining capacity to accommodate the entire oil flow to the engine. Strainers are frequently installed in parallel, or a duplex unit is used, so that one element can be cleaned while the other is allowed to function.

The second requirement in oil treatment is the filtering and purifying process. Various materials are used for this purpose, such as unbleached cotton waste, other forms of cotton and cellulose, and fuller's earth or activated clay. Certain other cleaning devices, known as edge-type filters, consist of stacks of paper or accurately-formed metal discs. The filtering action results when the oil is forced to flow through the fine clearances existing between the discs or plates making up the assembly. A similar principle is used in other devices where cotton thread or metal wire is carefully wound on a mandrel to a prescribed clearance between successive coils.

Fuller's earth or activated clay are very effective filter materials, and are also useful in reducing acidic contamination because of their ability to adsorb the soluble impurities. If lubricating oil containing additives is used, particularly those additives having special engine cleaning properties, filters using fuller's earth or activated clay should not be used as these materials may remove some of the additives, thereby changing the characteristics of the oil.

The use of cotton-waste or cellulose filters is generally recommended in place of the earth type for use with detergent or other additive-type oils.

To be effective, filters must be cleaned and serviced periodically. Excessive water contamination or low temperature ("wet") sludges may cause a filter to become clogged and inoperative in a very short time.

Full flow filters are considerably larger than by-pass filters but may be recommended by the engine manufacturer under certain operating conditions. A by-pass filter is supplied with oil by a branch from the main pressure line, and the filtered oil is returned to the engine oil sump or engine system.

Another method of operation is to install a separate pump for the filter and to pass the entire engine oil charge through the filter at regular intervals, say once a week or once a day. Several modifications of this method are used; the most popular uses two complete charges of oil, one charge being used in the engine while the other is being cleaned. Such a system is known as the batch method.

Reclaimers.—These are usually earth type filters with arrangements for heating the oil so that the action between the oil and the earth is accelerated and intensified. The higher temperature assists in driving off any moisture and to some extent any fuel oil dilution. Excessively high purifying temperatures may overtreat the lubricant, and accelerate additive loss. Therefore in some units, a vacuum pump is furnished, the vacuum making possible the removal of vapors without dangerously overheating the oil. Reclaimers may be operated on either the continuous by-pass or batch principle.

Centrifuges.—Centrifugal methods of oil purification have been popular, especially on shipboard since the centrifuge is effective in removing water from oil. However, some of the contamination is oxidation products having nearly the same specific gravity as the oil. Under this circumstance, the centrifuge works at a very low efficiency and is not always able to clean the oil as effectively as some other methods. In large systems or services where water may have to be removed, a centrifuge may be used ahead of a filter so that water and heavy contaminants will be removed before filtering. The user should take advantage of the oil supplier's con-

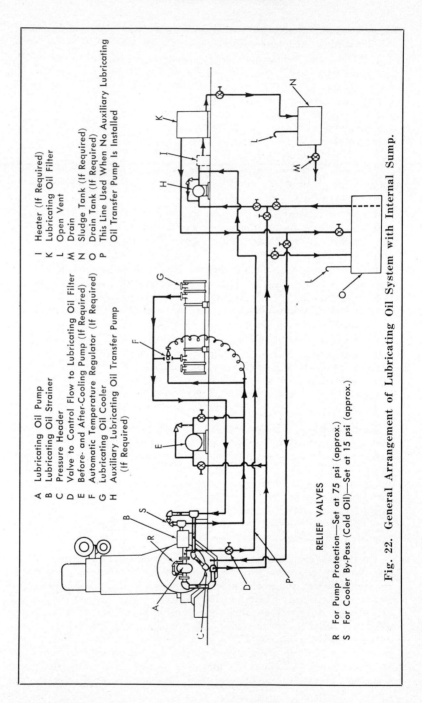

A   Lubricating Oil Pump
B   Lubricating Oil Strainer
C   Pressure Header
D   Valve to Control Flow to Lubricating Oil Filter
E   Before- and After-Cooling Pump (If Required)
F   Automatic Temperature Regulator (If Required)
G   Lubricating Oil Cooler
H   Auxiliary Lubricating Oil Transfer Pump
　　(If Required)

I   Heater (If Required)
K   Lubricating Oil Filter
L   Open Vent
M   Drain
N   Sludge Tank (If Required)
O   Drain Tank (If Required)
P   This Line Used When No Auxiliary Lubricating
　　Oil Transfer Pump Is Installed

RELIEF VALVES

R   For Pump Protection—Set at 75 psi (approx.)
S   For Cooler By-Pass (Cold Oil)—Set at 15 psi (approx.)

Fig. 22. General Arrangement of Lubricating Oil System with Internal Sump.

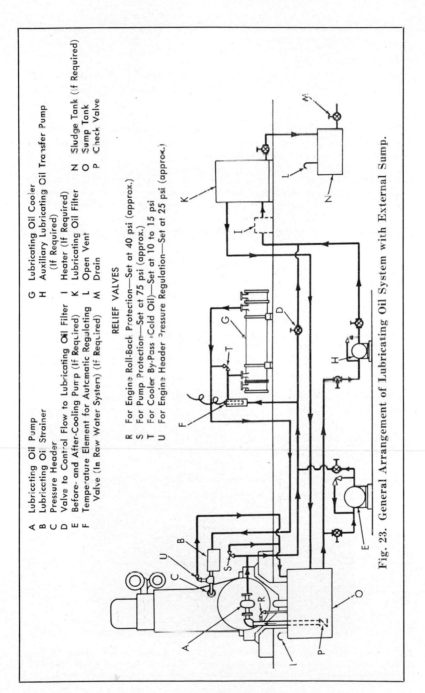

A Lubricating Oil Pump
B Lubricating Oil Strainer
C Pressure Header
D Valve to Control Flow to Lubricating Oil Filter
E Before- and After-Cooling Pump (If Required)
F Temperature Element for Automatic Regulating Valve (In Raw Water System) (If Required)

G Lubricating Oil Cooler
H Auxiliary Lubricating Oil Transfer Pump (If Required)
I Heater (If Required)
K Lubricating Oil Filter
L Open Vent
M Drain

N Sludge Tank (If Required)
O Sump Tank
P Check Valve

RELIEF VALVES

R For Engine Roll-Back Protection—Set at 40 psi (approx.)
S For Pump Protection—Set at 75 psi (approx.)
T For Cooler By-Pass (Cold Oil)—Set at 10 to 15 psi
U For Engine Header Pressure Regulation—Set at 25 psi (approx.)

Fig. 23. General Arrangement of Lubricating Oil System with External Sump.

sulting service in determining the proper method of handling and conditioning the lubricating oil.

Oil Coolers.—These are heat exchangers, usually of the conventional shell and tube type. It is important that coolers be of adequate size, as heat transfer capacity is lost rapidly as the cooling surfaces become dirty. Cooler surfaces must be kept clean on both the water and the oil sides. It is desirable to arrange a by-pass around the cooler which will permit the lubricating oil to reach a normal temperature when starting a cold engine. Means of preheating the oil may also be provided.

Instrumentation.—Every lubricating oil system requires certain devices that indicate its functioning at all times. The simplest power plant may have merely a visible-flow indicator or perhaps only a pressure gage. More elaborate installations will have complete outfits of gages and thermometers to serve every portion of a complex system.

Automatic Alarms and Protective Devices.—Much accidental damage has been prevented by automatic devices designed to signal the operators when improper conditions develop unexpectedly during operation. These are usually pressure- and temperature-controlled electric switches wired to visible or audible alarms. They are adjusted to function when the oil pressure becomes too low, or if the oil temperature becomes too high. If desired, the controls can be arranged so as to stop the engine automatically when proper conditions are not maintained.

Piping Diagrams.—As indicated above, arrangements of the lubricating oil system may vary considerably due to the requirements of the particular installation. Figs. 22 and 23 show typical piping arrangements for engines with internal and external oil sumps, respectively.

Fully automatic four-cycle dual fuel three-engine power plant at the A.E.C. Sandia Base, Albuquerque, New Mexico. Engines are started automatically in predetermined sequence as required by load.

CHAPTER TEN

Lubricating Oil Characteristics and General
Specifications

Lubrication is the complete or partial separation of adjacent moving surfaces by the use of suitable fluid or semi-fluid materials, in order to keep friction, with resultant wear and power loss, within safe and economical limits. Such materials are called lubricants and at normal temperatures may range from light oils which are liquids to greases which are in a plastic or semi-fluid state. Oils are invariably used to lubricate the engine proper, but greases are occasionally used in certain engine accessory equipment.

Lubricating oils may be mineral, animal or vegetable. The mineral oil is produced from petroleum, and for engine lubrication purposes is used to the exclusion of almost all others.

As found in their original state, crude oils are complex mixtures of many different hydrocarbon compounds, each of which has individual characteristics and properties. They also contain sulfur, nitrogen and oxygen compounds as well as inorganic salts which are removed wholly or in part on refining. Finished lubricants may contain up to 2 percent sulfur, as sulphur compounds. By proper refining treatment, the various fractions of the original oil are separated, one or more finally appearing as the base stock used for making lubricating oil. Because of the large number of individual hydrocarbons composing crude oil, it has not been possible to separate the crude into each of its constituents; commercial lubricants are therefore mixtures of a great many complex hydrocarbons.

Classification of Oils.—Crude oils are frequently described as being "paraffinic," "naphthenic" or "mixed-base." These are arbitrary terms derived from certain physical characteristics of the crude. The term "paraffinic" results from the fact that most of the crudes first discovered in this country were found to contain wax or paraffin. Others, discovered at a later date, gave asphaltic residues, and have therefore come to be known as asphaltic, or more properly, as naphthenic oils. Still other crudes were found to possess the characteristics of both paraffin and naphthenic oils, and hence have come to be called intermediate or mixed-base.

Generally speaking, for oil fractions having a given distillation temperature range, the paraffinic fractions are lower in specific gravity than naphthenic fractions.

A large number of sub-classifications of finished oils can be made, based on the type of base stock, the methods of refining and supplementary treatment used in manufacture, and the additives used.

Within any classification, oils of various viscosities are available to suit the particular requirements of a given engine.

These classifications do not describe the worth or value of a lubricating oil. Excellent products are available made from stocks of naphthenic base, of paraffinic base, and of a large variety of intermediate and mixed stocks; and by one or more of the many refining processes.

In recent years two general types of lubricating oils have been in use. The "straight" mineral oils are produced entirely from petroleum through the elimination of undesired constituents by suitable refining treatments. The "additive" oils are those in which one or more desirable characteristics have been enhanced by the addition of certain oil-soluble compounds to refined mineral oil. Additives are used singly or in combination principally to inhibit or slow down oxidation, to increase film strength, to keep solids in a finely divided state and to hold them in suspension (detergency), to improve the viscosity index, to lower the pour point, to decrease friction and wear under extreme-pressure conditions, to reduce foaming, and to inhibit rusting or corrosion.

The recommendations of the engine manufacturer plus the experience and skill of a long established, reputable oil company are the best assurance of the suitability of a lubricating oil offered for use in a particular engine.

Analysis of Oils.—For the purpose of classifying and identifying new oils and to discover what changes occur in service with these oils, the engine manufacturers and oil refiners refer to numerous chemical and physical tests.

The activity of Committee D-2 on Petroleum Products and Lubricants of the American Society for Testing Materials* has resulted in the standardization of these tests.

Generally, the following tests of new oil are of significance to the operator of an engine power plant:

> Viscosity, Kinematic or Saybolt
> Viscosity Index
> Gravity, in degrees API or specific gravity
> Flash Point, in degrees F
> Fire Point, in degrees F
> Cloud Point, in degrees F
> Pour Point, in degrees F
> Carbon residue, in percent by weight
> Neutralization Value

The following tests are generally performed on a sample of used oil taken from the crankcase of an engine in order to determine whether the oil is suitable for further service:

---

* 1916 Race St., Philadelphia 3, Penna.

Viscosity, Kinematic or Saybolt
Gravity, in degrees API or specific gravity
Flash Point, in degrees F
Fuel Dilution
Ash
Analysis of Ash
Neutralization Value
Water

Adequate and representative sampling is important if any significance is to be placed on the results of the tests performed on the oil sample. Sampling procedures recommended by the engine manufacturer or oil supplier should be followed.

It is desirable to understand what these tests are and what they signify before discussing the properties of any particular grade of oil. The tests do not offer conclusive evidence of an oil's suitability for a particular service, but do enable oils to be distinguished from one another. These tests are outlined below and reference given to the appropriate ASTM and ASA* test where it applies. For specific information concerning these tests, a copy of ASTM Standards on Petroleum Products and Lubricants may be obtained from the American Society for Testing Materials.

Viscosity (ASTM D 88, D 445, ASA Z11.2).—Viscosity is the term used to describe the resistance to flow or internal shear of a liquid. The oil "body" or viscosity must be suited to the service conditions and design features of a given engine. Bearing surfaces must be sustained by oil films at the pressures, temperatures, clearances, and relative movements between surfaces encountered in engine operation. Oil fluidity requires consideration when low-temperature starting conditions are encountered. Oils which are too viscous at reduced temperatures will not flow readily to bearing areas, and starvation of the bearings may result; also there is an increase in the frictional drag on the engine.

In the United States, viscosity is usually expressed for commercial purposes in SSU, from the name of an instrument used to determine this property. In using the Saybolt Universal viscosimeter, the viscosity is equal to the number of seconds required for a 60 cc sample to flow through the orifice of the instrument at a standard test temperature.

In recent years there has been a trend toward the use of kinematic viscosity instead of Saybolt viscosity. Kinematic viscosity is a more convenient measure of viscosity for oils that are used in a wide range of temperatures. Kinematic viscosity is the ratio of absolute viscosity to density. The unit of kinematic viscosity is the stoke, or, more commonly, the centistoke. It is a function of the measured efflux time, that is, the time required for a fixed volume of sample,

---

* American Standards Association, 70 E. 45th St., New York 17, N. Y.

Table 1—Viscosity Comparison Chart[1]

Saybolt Universal Viscosity,[2] Seconds At 100 F	Kinematic Viscosity, Centistokes At 100 F	Redwood No. 1 Viscosity, Redwood Seconds At 100 F	Engler Viscosity, Degrees Engler At 100 F
32.6	2.0	30.5	1.14
34	2.4	31.5	1.17
36	3.0	33.0	1.22
38	3.6	34.6	1.27
40	4.3	36.3	1.33
42	4.9	37.9	1.39
44	5.5	39.5	1.44
46	6.2	41.3	1.50
48	6.8	42.9	1.55
50	7.4	44.5	1.60
55	8.9	48.7	1.74
60	10.3	52.7	1.86
65	11.7	57.1	1.99
70	13.1	61.5	2.13
75	14.4	65.8	2.26
80	15.7	70.2	2.40
85	17.0	74.7	2.54
90	18.2	79.0	2.67
95	19.4	83.4	2.80
100	20.6	87.8	2.94
110	22.9	96.5	3.20
120	25.3	105.5	3.49
130	27.5	114.1	3.76
140	29.8	123.2	4.04
160	34.3	140.9	4.61
180	38.7	158.5	5.17
200	43.2	176.5	5.75
225	48.6	198.2	6.44
250	54.0	220.0	7.11
300	64.9	264.1	8.54
350	75.8	307.1	9.97
400	86.6	350.9	11.39
450	97.4	394.8	12.82
500	108.3	438.7	14.24
550	119.1	482.5	15.66
600	129.9	526.4	17.09
650	140.7	570.2	18.51
700	151.6	614.1	19.94
800	173.2	701.8	22.78
900	194.9	789.6	25.63
1000	216.5	877.3	28.48
1500	324.8	1316.0	42.72
2000	433.0	1754.6	56.96
2500	541.3	2193.3	71.20

[1] From April 1945 issue of "Lubrication" published by The Texas Company.

[2] There is no maximum limit to viscosity to be measured by the Saybolt Universal Viscosimeter but, in general, liquids having an outflow time in the order of 1000 seconds and higher, Saybolt Universal, are tested by means of the Saybolt Furol Viscosimeter. The outflow time of the Furol instrument is approximately one-tenth of the Universal. The word "Furol" is a contraction of the phrase "fuel and road oils."

contained in a glass viscosimeter, to flow through a calibrated capillary under an accurately reproducible head of liquid and at a closely controlled temperature.

Table 1, Viscosity Comparison Chart, shows the relationship between Saybolt, Kinematic, Redwood and Engler viscosities at 100 F. Viscosity is usually measured in the laboratory at one or more standard temperatures, such as 0, 100 or 210 F. The viscosity of an oil changes with temperature, becoming greater at low temperatures and less at high temperatures.

Viscosity of SAE Grades.—Lubricating oils are sometimes purchased by SAE (Society of Automotive Engineers)* viscosity numbers to designate the desired viscosity or grade of oil. These numbers have no significance as to quality or character. The SAE viscosity numbers constitute a classification for crankcase lubricating oils in terms of viscosity only (See Table 2). Viscosity numbers without an additional symbol are based on the viscosity at 210 F. Viscosity numbers with the additional symbol W are based on the viscosity at 0 F. The viscosity of oils included in this classification for use in crankcases shall be not less than 39 SSU at 210 F.

Table 2—SAE Viscosities

Viscosity Range, Saybolt Universal Sec.

SAE Viscosity Number	At 0 F		At 210 F	
	Min.	Max.	Min.	Max.
5W	—	4,000	—	—
10W	6,000 (Note A)	Less than 12,000	—	—
20W	12,000 (Note B)	48,000	—	—
20	—	—	45	Less than 58
30	—	—	58	Less than 70
40	—	—	70	Less than 85
50	—	—	85	110

Note A—Minimum viscosity at 0 F may be waived provided viscosity at 210 F is not below 40 sec, Saybolt Universal.

Note B—Minimum viscosity at 0 F may be waived provided viscosity at 210 F is not below 45 sec, Saybolt Universal.

Viscosity for Cold Starting.—Many engines are so located that they must be started when extremely cold. Some specifications have given 30,000 SSU as the highest permissible lubricating oil viscosity at the starting temperature. However, the starting of cold engines may be difficult even with low viscosity lubricants. Hence

---

* 485 Lexington Ave., New York 17, N. Y.

the preferred method is to keep the engine warm in a suitably heated enclosure or to use heating equipment to raise the temperature of the lubricating oil and the jacket water prior to the start.

Viscosity Index (ASTM D 567, ASA Z11.45).—This is an empirical number used to indicate the relative change in viscosity of an oil for a given temperature change. If two oils of different types of base stocks have the same viscosity at 100 F, one may have a higher viscosity than the other at 210 F. Paraffinic oils in general have a low rate of viscosity change with change in temperature, and a particular paraffinic oil was arbitrarily assigned an index of 100; naphthenic oils have a high rate of viscosity change, and a particular naphthenic oil was arbitrarily given an index of zero. Hence, the viscosity index, or VI, of any oil shows how its viscosity changes with a change in temperature as compared with these two standards.

Viscosity index is important especially if an engine is required to operate under widely varying temperature conditions. It is also important in regard to low temperature starting because a high VI oil will have a relatively low viscosity at low temperatures compared with low VI oils.

Gravity (ASTM D 287, ASA Z11.31).—The relative weight of an oil is indicated by the API gravity number. This value may be determined from the specific gravity by use of the following formula:

$$\text{API Gravity (degrees)} = \frac{141.5}{\text{Sp gr at 60 F}} - 131.5$$

Gravity is of little significance as an index of quality or usefulness of a lubricating oil.

Flash Point (ASTM D 92, ASA Z11.6).—This is the lowest oil temperature at which flashes of flame can be seen when the oil is heated in standard test equipment and a small flame is applied to the oil vapors.

Fire Point (ASTM D 92, ASA Z11.6).—This is the lowest temperature at which the vapors, created when oil is heated under controlled conditions, will ignite and burn in air for a period of five seconds upon application of a flame.

Cloud and Pour Point (ASTM D 97, ASA Z11.5).—The cloud point is the temperature at which oil becomes cloudy, as the result of the formation of wax crystals. The pour point is the lowest temperature at which the oil will flow of its own accord, measured under standard test conditions. Because pour point is indicative of the pumpability of an oil, a low pour point is to be desired if an engine must be started after being exposed for some time to cold weather, especially if the oil is required to flow by gravity. The pour point is not the only factor influencing ease of starting a cold engine.

Carbon Residue (ASTM D 189, D 524, ASA Z11.25).—This is sometimes called Conradson Carbon and is the carbonaceous residue formed during evaporation and pyrolysis of an oil sample in a standard apparatus. The residue is not composed entirely of carbon but also contains hydrocarbons formed by pyrolysis. The residue is expressed as a percentage, by weight, of the original sample. This is sometimes believed to indicate the amount of carbon that may be deposited in an engine. Actually, because of the many accessory factors found in field operation, Conradson Carbon by itself is of little real value as a gage of oil performance as far as engine deposits are concerned. The percentage of ash containing additives in additive type oils increases the apparent Conradson Carbon and makes the test valueless except for identification purposes. Carbon residue tests are always run on the full sample in the case of lubricating oils and never on 10 percent residuum as is often the case for light fuel oils.

Recently there has been a trend toward replacing the Conradson Carbon Residue test with the more expedient Ramsbottom Test (ASTM D 524, ASA Z 11.47). The latter test is also used in order to provide some indication of the relative coke-forming propensity of lubricating oils.

Neutralization Value (ASTM D 664, D 974, ASA Z11.59).—This is a test to determine the acid or basic constituents in new or used engine oils. The value is usually expressed as a "neutralization number" with the added designation "alkaline," "basic," or "negative" if the result is not on the acid side.

The acid number, a term often used, is the quantity of potassium hydroxide, expressed in milligrams, that is required to neutralize (titrate) all acidic constitutents present in one gram of the sample oil. Correspondingly, the base number is the quantity of acid, expressed in terms of the equivalent number of milligrams of potassium hydroxide, that is required to neutralize (titrate) all basic constituents present in one gram of sample oil.

A number of different laboratory methods are in general use; two of the more popular are ASTM D 974 "Neutralization Value (Acid and Base Numbers) by Color-Indicator Titration" and ASTM D 664 "Neutralization Value (Acid and Base Numbers) by Potentiometric Titration." It is important to recognize that values may vary to a considerable degree when obtained by different methods and are not always closely reproducible using a single method. Comparison is often difficult or without significance.

It is equally important to recognize that the interpretation of the readings calls for experience and the consideration of many other factors. The presence of additives in the oil may, under some circumstances, so modify the test results as to make any generalized rules impossible.

Since many of the products resulting from the oxidation of oil are acidic to a greater or less degree, the increase in neutralization value (acid number) over that of new oil when taken into consideration with other factors is a partial indicator of the extent of oil oxidation. A number of other causes, particularly contamination from the fuel oil, can increase the neutralization reading; therefore, the results require careful examination. As indicated previously, the tests are difficult to make with accuracy, and small differences in reading are usually without significance. The principal use of the neutralization value is to show by periodic analysis the rate of change taking place in the used oil. This rate of change should be discussed with the oil supplier for the purpose of determining its significance.

Oil Deterioration.—Under the usual conditions of service in engines, the lubricants are exposed to high temperatures and pressures, are often finely divided as a spray or mist intimately mixed with air, and are subjected to the catalytic effects of various metals, metallic compounds and other contaminants. The invariable results are changes in the character of some of the molecules of the oil. The high temperatures may cause the polymerization of certain hydrocarbon compounds into other complex combinations. The contact with air results in oxidation and the production of gums, resins, and acids. The catalytic effect of several usually present contaminants further accelerates chemical changes.

The products of oil deterioration are an almost infinite series of compounds, differing with each oil and with each set of operating conditions.

The characteristics of the fuel oil, and the condition and adjustment of the injection equipment, have a large influence on the condition of the lubricating oil. Many lubricating oil contaminants are products of combustion. Soot, ash and partially burned or raw fuel oil mix with the lubricant on the cylinder walls and take an intimate part in accelerating the rate of deterioration of the lubricating oil. High fuel sulfur content may also accelerate the rate of oil deterioration.

The extent of oil contamination depends on several factors, among which are fuel, lubricant, elapsed hours of operation, load, engine condition, etc. The contaminating substances should be removed before trouble is caused.

The contaminants may be removed by purifying so that the oil can continue in service. Another method is to discard part or all of the contaminated oil. If only a portion of the oil is discarded it is replaced by clean oil so that the average level of contamination is low.

The most desirable method will depend on the type of engine, the service to which it is subjected and the type of oil used. The color alone of the oil, especially of the additive type, is no criterion by which to judge its usefulness. The dark color of used additive oils is due to their dispersency which holds contaminants in suspension.

Service Results.—Chemical and physical tests under laboratory conditions are helpful in assisting experienced investigators in their work. However, it is a widely accepted fact that actual service in an engine is the only worthwhile and final test of the serviceability of any particular lubricant. Oils showing good results in laboratory tests have not always given corresponding satisfaction in all kinds of actual service, while other oils, of poorer laboratory performance, have given fine results in one or many engine designs and under actual operating conditions.

Laboratory tests must be correlated with engine condition because, after all, such things as absence of deposits and low rates of wear are more important than the physical and chemical characteristics of the used oil taken out of the engine. Sometimes the latter may be correlated with the former and then the operator has a real yardstick for checking on oil change periods and engine condition. Unfortunately this correlation may vary considerably between engines and types of service.

The engine itself is the best judge of good oils, and the reputation and experience of the oil refiner must be relied on to furnish, according to his best judgment, the oil which may be expected to return the best results in each instance.

Three 4380 hp, 16 cylinder, four-cycle gas engines in the Saskatchewan Power Corporation's Kindersley plant. Engines are equipped with turbo-expanders.

CHAPTER ELEVEN

Fuel Oil Storage and Handling Systems

The fuel oil storage and handling systems of a Diesel, gas-Diesel, or dual fuel engine plant includes:

1. Unloading facilities to take fuel oil from the carrier (barge, tank car, pipeline or tank truck) and transfer it to storage.

2. Storage to hold the fuel oil until it is to be used.

3. Transfer equipment to deliver fuel oil from storage to the engine.

4. Pressure gages, thermometers and meters.

5. Cleaning facilities (strainers, filters, purifiers, centrifuges, etc.)

6. If necessary, it may include heating equipment to heat the fuel oil in order that it may be more easily handled or more effectively cleaned.

In addition, it follows that there must be a system of piping connecting these facilities.

Fuel Oil Delivery and Storage.—The storage capacity depends principally on the manner of delivery of fuel oil. For gas-Diesel or dual fuel installations the fuel oil storage capacity also depends on whether the gas fuel supply is on an interruptible basis or not. Usually fuel oil is obtained from tank cars, tank trucks or oil barges—in that order of frequency. Diesel plants used for pipeline pumping may use crude oil out of the line, and plants in or near a refinery may have pipeline delivery.

Tank Car Delivery.—Standard tank cars vary in capacity from 6,000 to 10,000 gallons. No matter how small the Diesel plant may be, if it is planned to buy oil in tank cars, there must be storage in excess of that capacity in order that the car may be emptied into storage while there is still oil on hand for operating. A good plan is to install capacity to last over at least twice the period normally between shipments.

Tank Truck Delivery.—Tank trucks vary in size from 600 to 6,000 gallons capacity, the minimum compartments being approximately 200 gallons. Storage tank capacity sufficient to accommodate a full tank truck is convenient to both the supplier and the user, and may result in some reduction in price.

Barge Delivery.—Almost any quantity of fuel oil may be obtained in a barge delivery, but there is almost always a minimum shipment which is required to obtain the best price.

Influence of Plant Location.—The location of the plant may impose conditions as to storage capacity which overrule the recommendations based upon manner of delivery alone. Large above-ground tanks would be unsightly in a residential district, and space for tank storage might be too costly in a business district. Local ordinances should be investigated to see what restrictions, if any, must be observed in regard to size of tankage and storage arrangements.

Influence of Market.—Users located at a distance from fuel oil distribution centers should install more storage capacity than those near such centers, in order to be more independent of delays in shipping. Excess storage capacity also places a user in a position to take advantage of favorable market conditions.

Calculation of Storage Capacity.—The average Diesel plant on central station duty will generate about 2500 net kwhr per year per kw installed, at a conservative rate (for easy calculation) of about 10 net kwhr per gallon of fuel oil. This corresponds approximately to 4 barrels of fuel (42 gal per bbl) per year per horsepower installed (6 bbl per kilowatt installed). Thus a 2000 hp municipal plant would use about 8,000 bbl, or 336,000 gal, of fuel oil per year. Monthly incoming tank car shipments make a convenient schedule; this would mean approximately 28,000 gal incoming per month. Enough storage capacity to last over two periods would call for about 60,000 gal of tankage.

The district in which the plant is to be located might impose restrictions which result in less storage and more frequent shipments. With no such restrictions, the distance from the source of supply might be so great that more capacity would be desirable. Excess tank capacity costs very little and often proves to be an excellent investment.

Number of Tanks to Install.—If possible, the main storage should be divided into two or more tanks. Fuel oil tanks do not need to be cleaned very frequently, but when cleaning time does come around, the procedure need not interrupt operations if there is more than one tank. If the fuel is high in water or sediment, or both, multiple tanks permit settling, and also provide a means for segregating clean fuel after settling or centrifuging.

Underwriters' Regulations.—The "Standards No. 30 of the National Board of Fire Underwriters* for Storage, Handling and Use of Flammable Liquids" should be scrupulously observed. Any local and state regulations governing such installations should also be investigated and observed. All reputable tank manufacturers are acquainted with these rules, and are accustomed, as a routine matter, to construct tanks which conform to them.

---

* 85 John Street, New York 38, N. Y.

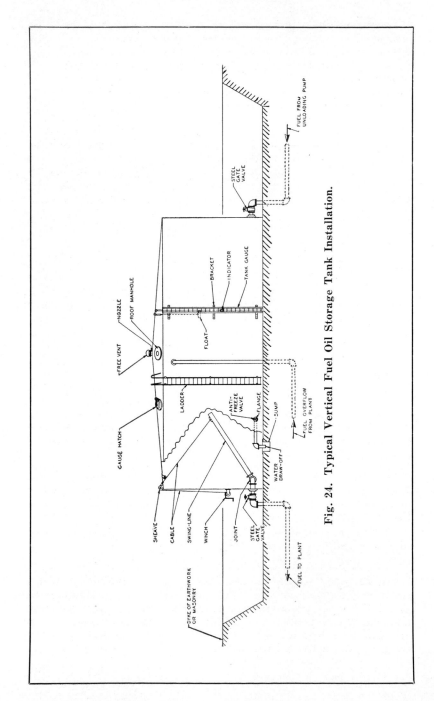

Fig. 24. Typical Vertical Fuel Oil Storage Tank Installation.

Construction and Layout of Tanks.—Tanks may be either horizontal or vertical, the choice depending on size and local conditions; horizontal tanks are generally used where capacity does not exceed approximately 30,000 gallons. All storage tanks should be provided with a suitable drain or other provision for removing water and sediment from the bottom of the tank. Tanks shall preferably be made of steel or black iron, without galvanizing. Particularly if water is present, zinc from the galvanizing can enter the oil in the form of a soluble soap and result in injection nozzle deposits. Some metals, such as copper, promote the gum forming tendencies of petroleum fuels in storage.

In the case of vertical tanks, such as illustrated by Figure 24, the Standards issued by American Petroleum Institute* as API Specification for Welded Oil Storage Tanks, API Standard 12 C, 15th Edition, 1958, or current edition should be followed. This tank is drained by the use of a suction pump attached to the water draw-off connection.

Typical horizontal tank arrangements are shown in Fig. 25 and Fig. 26 illustrating above ground and below ground installations respectively.

Tank Gaging.—Every Diesel plant should have adequate facilities for gaging fuel oil at the main storage to indicate proper time for reordering. In this connection it should be remembered that accurate gaging is affected by fuel oil temperature as well as by whether the tank is straight or slightly inclined. If doubt exists, the oil supplier should be able to give assistance in calibrating the tank gages. Further assistance may be obtained by referring to the ASTM Manual on Measurement and Sampling of Petroleum Products, Third Edition, December, 1957, or current edition. Where more than one engine is installed, it is desirable to provide measuring equipment to determine the fuel oil consumption of individual units.

Service Tanks.—The engine room supply of cleaned fuel oil is provided by a service tank or tanks located in the engine room or outside the building, as required. A separate tank is recommended for each unit.

The National Board of Fire Underwriters has rules governing the size and location of service tanks (NBFU No. 30, July 1954 or current edition).

Unloading System.—If the tank-car siding is higher than the top of the storage tank, the fuel oil may be drained into storage by gravity. This is not always the situation, and for some plants an unloading pump is necessary. Suggested piping and fittings for this are shown in Fig. 27. This illustration shows the pump suction connected to the top of the tank car. There is an increasing tendency

---

* 50 W. 50th St., New York 20, N. Y.

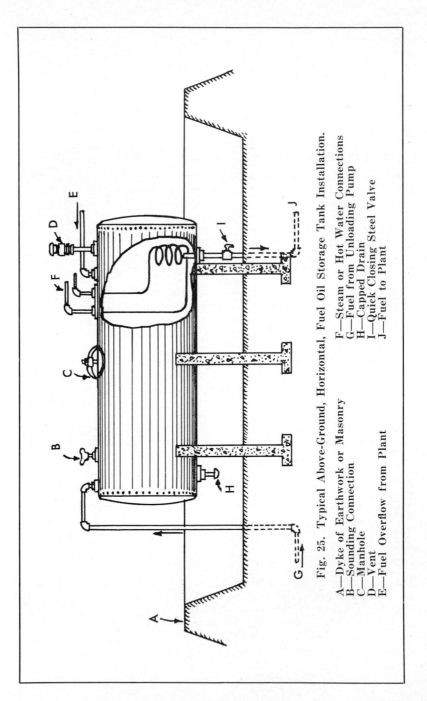

Fig. 25. Typical Above-Ground, Horizontal, Fuel Oil Storage Tank Installation.

A—Dyke of Earthwork or Masonry   F—Steam or Hot Water Connections
B—Sounding Connection   G—Fuel from Unloading Pump
C—Manhole   H—Capped Drain
D—Vent   I—Quick Closing Steel Valve
E—Fuel Overflow from Plant   J—Fuel to Plant

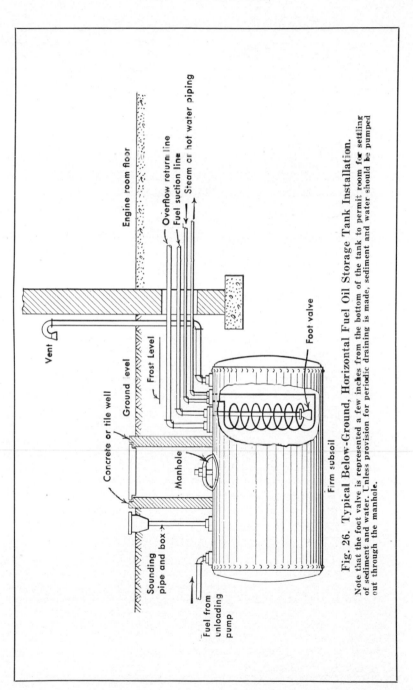

Fig. 26. **Typical Below-Ground, Horizontal Fuel Oil Storage Tank Installation.**

Note that the foot valve is represented a few inches from the bottom of the tank to permit room for settling of sediment and water. Unless provision for periodic draining is made, sediment and water should be pumped out through the manhole.

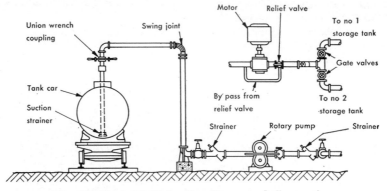

Fig. 27. **Fuel Oil Unloading Pump and Connections.**

for plant operators to unload in this manner rather than from the bottom, as this results in improved fuel cleanliness because any dirt or water which may be present will generally settle to the bottom of the tank.

Unloading pumps are usually of the rotary type and large enough to unload the incoming shipment in less than the demurrage time. There should be a relief valve in the discharge, by-passing back to the suction, to guard against closed circuits.

Some tank cars are equipped with coils for heating by steam or hot water. If the plant is to be located in a cold climate, and especially if heavy fuel oil is to be used, there should be arrangements for such steam or hot water to prepare the fuel oil for handling.

Transfer System.—Fuel oil from the main storage is transferred to service tanks by a transfer pump, which may be of the rotary or plunger type. This pump may be hand-operated in small sizes; larger sizes are usually power-driven. If pumping is to be automatically controlled by the level in each service tank, there is usually a separate pump for each such tank. The usual layout of transfer pump, service tank and connections is shown in Fig. 28. A large duplex strainer, or other cleaning equipment, between the main storage and the transfer pump is recommended.

Gaseous Fuel System.*—Most installations of gas-Diesel and dual fuel Diesel engines are usually made adjacent to a main gas pipeline or gas distribution system. In general the gas supplied is clean, dry natural gas. Fig. 29 shows a typical dual-fuel piping installation. Provision should be made for pressure regulators, meters, reservoirs, valving, thermometers and gages as shown. Gas vent lines and lines from relief valves should always be carried outside the building and never connected to drains or sewers. In case the gas supply pressure is below the engine manufacturer's requirements,

---

* For further details of gaseous fuel system see Chapter 13.

compressors may be necessary to boost the gas pressure to the required level.

In installations where the gas supply rate is variable, such as sewage disposal plants, large gas holders may be installed to store the gas during periods of heavy flow so as to provide a steady supply to the engine at all times.

Heating and Cleaning of Fuel Oil other than Residual.— The equipment required for heating and cleaning will vary widely depending upon the characteristics of the fuel to be used. Where light fuels, such as ASTM Diesel fuel grades 1D, 2D and 4D, are used, no heating facilities are required except in abnormal circumstances of severe cold, and satisfactory cleaning can be accomplished by a duplex strainer in the fuel supply system, augmented by the fuel strainer, and filters normally furnished as regular engine equipment.

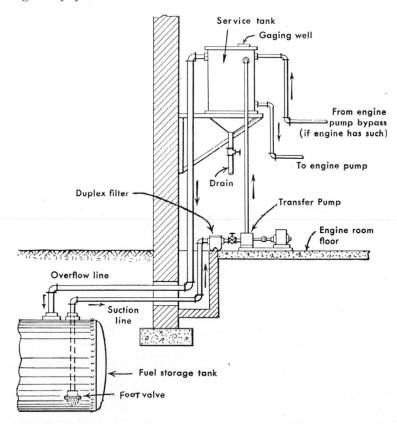

Service tank

Gaging well

From engine pump bypass (if engine has such)

To engine pump

Drain

Duplex filter

Transfer Pump

Engine room floor

Overflow line

Suction line

Fuel storage tank

Foot valve

Fig. 28. Typical Layout of Transfer Pump and Service Tank, for Engines Requiring Overhead Service Tanks.

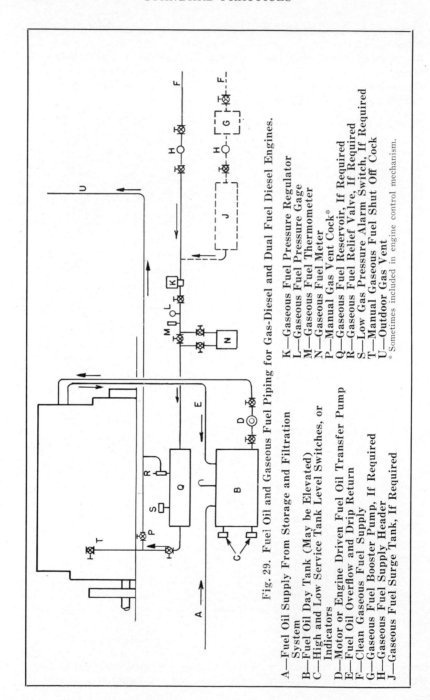

Fig. 29. Fuel Oil and Gaseous Fuel Piping for Gas-Diesel and Dual Fuel Diesel Engines.

A—Fuel Oil Supply From Storage and Filtration System
B—Fuel Oil Day Tank (May be Elevated)
C—High and Low Service Tank Level Switches, or Indicators
D—Motor or Engine Driven Fuel Oil Transfer Pump
E—Fuel Oil Overflow and Drip Return
F—Clean Gaseous Fuel Supply
G—Gaseous Fuel Booster Pump, If Required
H—Gaseous Fuel Supply Header
J—Gaseous Fuel Surge Tank, If Required

K—Gaseous Fuel Pressure Regulator
L—Gaseous Fuel Pressure Gage
M—Gaseous Fuel Thermometer
N—Gaseous Fuel Meter
P—Manual Gas Vent Cock*
Q—Gaseous Fuel Reservoir, If Required
R—Gaseous Fuel Relief Valve, If Required
S—Low Gas Pressure Alarm Switch, If Required
T—Manual Gaseous Fuel Shut Off Cock
U—Outdoor Gas Vent
* Sometimes included in engine control mechanism.

Heating of the fuel may be required for three reasons: (1) to enable the fuel to be pumped from the storage tank to the engine, (2) to permit more effective cleaning, either by filtering or centrifuging or both, and (3) to permit proper operation of the injection pumps and injectors.

Transfer of the oil from the storage tank is affected by both the pour point and the viscosity of the fuel. High viscosity fuels may become difficult to handle at temperatures even above their pour point. The necessity for heating the oil in order to pump it from the tank may be avoided by specifying sufficiently low viscosity and pour point requirements; however, this may lead to a higher priced oil. Installation of heating facilities will minimize handling difficulties, and by permitting the use of a lower priced product may be quite profitable.

Where fuels are to be cleaned by centrifuging, it has been found that temperatures above 150 F, into the centrifuge, often result in more effective cleaning. Since the most suitable temperature varies depending on the particular type of oil being used, the proper temperature can be determined only by experiment. Precautionary measures must be taken if fuel is heated above its flash point. The oil supplier may be helpful in this respect.

Proper operation of injection pumps and injectors, particularly with respect to the proper injector spray characteristics, depends largely on the viscosity of the fuel. Limiting requirements may be obtained from the engine builder, following which the oil supplier will be able to advise as to the proper temperature for the fuel. Most large engines, capable of using heavy fuels, require that the fuel be heated so that the viscosity at the injectors is 150 SSU or less. In extreme cases, where heavy fuels are used, this may require provision for fuel heating all the way to the injection valves.

In Fig. 26 a hot water or steam coil is shown surrounding the fuel suction pipe. For especially heavy fuels, this coil may be enlarged. A similar coil can be located in each service tank. Such a coil should have no joints within the tank. These arrangements should suffice for all but the heaviest grades of fuel oil.

The viscosity of most oils is reduced very rapidly with only a little heating. An oil of 5000 SSU viscosity at the pumping temperature is not suitable for handling, yet an average oil of that viscosity at 60 F will be reduced down to 400 SSU if heated to only about 130 F. Such a moderate application of heat does not call for an elaborate heating system and can be supplied by heat recovery from the engine. Some heavy oils may require an elaborate heating and extensive cleaning system involving the use of centrifuges and special filtration.

Any system for utilizing heavy oil requiring heating should have arrangements for starting and stopping an engine on light oil. The best layout is to have service tanks in pairs, one tank for light and one for heavy fuel oil. The two tanks should be connected to the

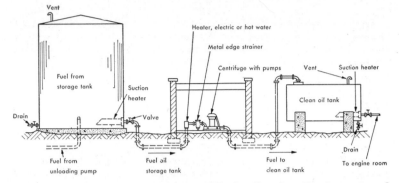

Fig. 30. Typical Layout of Storage Tank, Cleaning Equipment and Clean Oil Tank.

engine line by a three-way valve so that one tank or the other, but not both, is serving the engine. The engine piping system can then be cleared of heavy fuel before shutting down.

Impurities, if present, will not readily settle out of fuels having viscosities higher than about 150 SSU at the storage temperature. When such fuels contain more than about 0.1 percent sediment and water, it is advisable to purify them by a centrifuge and/or other means before they are fed to the engine. Proper use of this equipment will eliminate all the water and virtually all of the sediment.

The usual procedure is to draw the fuel by gravity or pump from the regular storage and force it through a closed tank or heat exchanger where it is heated by a steam or hot water coil to 180 F or higher. As mentioned previously, the optimum temperature depends on the oil and can be determined only by experiment, the best temperature being that at which the cleaning equipment removes the greatest amount of sediment.

After the fuel is heated and cleaned it goes to a clean oil tank. A diagram of these arrangements is shown in Fig. 30.

Heating and Cleaning of Residual Fuel Oil.—Increasing cost of distillate fuels in recent years has drawn considerable attention to the use of comparatively low cost residual fuels in Diesel engines. In many cases No. 5 or No. 6 fuels are being used economically; however, they require the use of additional equipment and some modification of operating procedures.

Figure 31 shows a typical basic piping diagram for a residual fuel oil system. Although steam heat generated by an oil fired boiler is shown for heating the fuel, electricity or waste heat may be employed. It is advisable to use thermostatically controlled heat to prevent fluctuations in viscosity.

The system may be divided into two stages: (1) between the storage tank and day tank; (2) between the day tank and engine. Each of these stages will be discussed.

In order to pump the fuel successfully it is generally advisable to provide a heated suction in the storage tank to maintain a pumping viscosity less than 5000 SSU or 500 SSF. Precautions should be taken to prevent any leaks in the heating systems inside the tanks. A fuel transfer pump operating continuously, with a spare unit as standby, discharges fuel through the primary heater, centrifuge and to the day tank.

Heating the day tank may not be necessary if it is insulated. The centrifuging temperature is maintained such that the viscosity range is 100 to 250 SSU for best results. The level in the day tank is controlled by a float actuated valve which permits the centrifuge to purify only the amount of fuel the engine consumes. Centrifuging at a slow rate increases the efficiency of the operation. The centrifuge is shut down for cleaning as required, and as added protection a standby centrifuge may be used if the expense is warranted.

In the second stage of the system the fuel is heated and filtered. The supply pump discharges through the secondary heater, filter, electric heater (optional), and then to the engine. A standby supply pump is recommended. Temperature of the fuel from the secondary heater should hold the viscosity in the range of 50 to 150 SSU for proper operation of the injection pumps and injectors. An insulated filter is necessary and although provision for heating is optional it has been found advantageous when first placing the system in operation or after shutdowns.

Provisions have been shown for draining the residual fuel day tank and purging the complete residual fuel oil system with light fuel by using only existing equipment. This is advantageous if the residual fuel system is shut down for any length of time as it may congeal, causing considerable inconvenience.

The size of the various pumps, heaters, centrifuges, filters, etc., will depend on the source of heat, specifications of residual fuel being used and the amount consumed.

The engine should always be started and stopped on light fuel. Before shutting down, the unit should operate on light fuel until all the residual fuel in the piping on the engines has been replaced.

Although the diagram is based on a one engine installation, it is possible to serve additional units by the application of pressure regulating valves or individual pumps to maintain a constant pressure in the residual fuel supply header.

Viscosity-Temperature Chart for Residual Fuels.—The viscosity of a residual fuel is a very important factor because a residual fuel must be preheated to temperatures which correspond to certain viscosities in order to be able to pump the fuel oil, clean it efficiently and inject it into the Diesel engine.

In the United States viscosity of residual fuels is ordinarily measured by the Saybolt Universal Viscosimeter in seconds (SSU) at 100 F or by the Saybolt Furol Viscosimeter in seconds (SSF)

at 122 F for fuel oils with flow times of more than 25 seconds
Furol. The viscosity chart, Fig. 32, is a means for determining the
viscosity of a fuel oil at various temperatures. The rate of change
in viscosity varies with different fuel oil. In order to obtain exact
values for the viscosity, it would be necessary to have the viscosity
taken at two temperatures, this second reading preferably at 210 F.
The viscosity chart is made for average rates of changes in viscosity
and is satisfactory for most cases. It also shows limiting viscosities
for pumping, centrifuging and fuel injection.

The upper viscosity range for pumping fuel oil is at a viscosity of
2000 to 5000 SSU depending on speed and type of pumps. The
usual range of viscosity for centrifuging is between 100 and 250
SSU. The best centrifuging viscosity and temperature depend on
the type of fuel oil and on the plant arrangement. The usual viscosity of the residual fuel at the injection system varies between 50
and 150 SSU. The desirable viscosity depends on the particular
design of the engine.

Detailed specifications of the residual fuel proposed should be
submitted to the engine builder who will make recommendations as
to its suitability and proper processing.

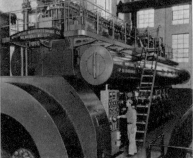

Shown above is an interior view
of the municipal power plant at
Ponca City, Oklahoma, which
operates 10 two-cycle Diesel and
dual fuel engines. The engines
range in size from 1250 horsepower to the 8500 horsepower
unit shown on the left which is
the largest dual fuel engine in
the world. These engines operate
on gas or residual fuel.

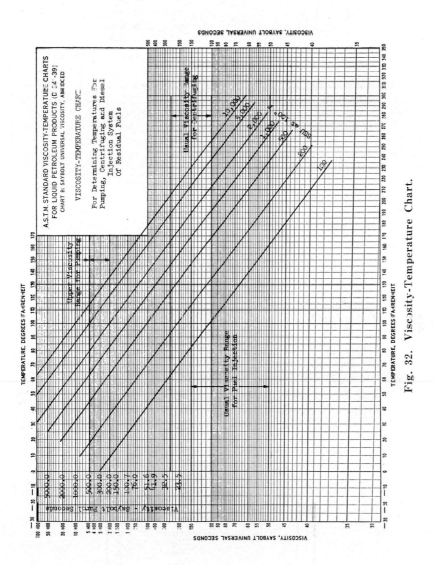

Fig. 32. Viscosity-Temperature Chart.

CHAPTER TWELVE

Characteristics and General Specifications
of Liquid Fuels for Diesel Engines

The petroleum industry produces liquid fuels generally conforming to either of two specifications: ASTM D 975 "Diesel Fuel Oils" (see Table 3) or ASTM D 396 "Fuel Oils" (see Table 4).

Selection of the most economical fuel for Diesel engines is dependent upon several variables: engine requirements, operating conditions, fuel quality, availability and cost. Engines vary widely in the grade of fuel required for satisfactory operation; in general, the high speed, high output engines require a higher quality fuel than the large, low speed types.

Fuel availability and quality vary somewhat with geographical location, with particular reference to the oil fields, oil refinery operation, and to local demands. Fuel price is affected by these factors, and also by available transportation means, such as barge connections or railroad sidings.

Other factors being equal, fuel price varies with quality. High cetane number, high volatility fuels are more expensive than low cetane, heavier type fuels. For any grade of fuel, careful control of uniformity generally carries a price premium, because of the operating limitations imposed on the refiner.

The engine manufacturer's recommendation is the logical starting point for selecting the fuel for an engine. These recommendations may subsequently be tempered, in view of experience and the local fuel situation, to obtain additional economies; however, such steps should be taken carefully.

Fuel Analysis—In recommending and in supplying Diesel fuel, engine manufacturers and refiners refer to numerous chemical and physical tests, specifying various characteristics of the fuel. These characteristics are useful when making purchases for duplicating fuels from the same sources but experience indicates that no specifications are a positive assurance of general suitability in an engine. Some of these tests have been found to correlate well with certain phases of engine operation, while others correlate only indirectly.

The following tests are generally conducted on fuel oil depending on the particular grade of fuel, as shown in Tables 3 and 4. To meet individual requirements additional tests may be requested such as High (Gross) Heat Value:

Gravity, in degrees API or specific gravity, since the two are mutually convertible.

Flash Point, by Pensky-Martens closed tester, in degrees F.

Water and Sediment, by centrifuge, in percent by volume.

Viscosity, in SSU @ 100 F, SSF @ 122 F or in centistokes at 100 F by the kinematic method.

Carbon Residue, in percent by weight.

Ash, in percent by weight.

Cloud Point, in degrees F.

Pour Point, in degrees F.

Sulfur, in percent by weight.

Corrosion Test, by copper strip method.

Ignition Quality, in cetane number.

Distillation, in degrees F.

The activity of Committee D-2 on Petroleum Products and Lubricants of the American Society for Testing Materials* has resulted in the standardization of these tests.

It is desirable to understand what these tests are and what they signify before discussing the properties of any particular grade of fuel. These tests are outlined below and reference given to the appropriate ASTM test. For specific information concerning these tests a copy of the ASTM Standards on Petroleum Products and Lubricants may be obtained from the American Society for Testing Materials.

In sending a sample of fuel to a testing laboratory it is advisable to specify the tests to be conducted, otherwise the laboratory may run tests that are not pertinent or may omit tests that would provide indicative data.

Specific Gravity and API Gravity (ASTM D 287, ASA Z11.31).

—The weight per unit volume of a fuel is expressed either in terms of Specific Gravity or of API Gravity.

For specific gravity, the weight of a given volume of material (that is, a quart or a gallon) is compared with the weight of an equal volume of fresh water. A liquid having the same weight as water for a given volume is said to have a specific gravity of 1.000. A liquid weighing twice as much as water, for a given volume, would have a specific gravity of 2.000, while a liquid weighing half as much as water, for a given volume, would have a specific gravity of 0.500. Accordingly, the heavier the liquid for a given volume, the higher is its specific gravity.

API gravity, which is more generally used for petroleum, refers to the American Petroleum Institute and the method standardized by the American Society for Testing Materials. According to this method the API gravity of water is 10.0. Liquids lighter than water have API gravities higher than 10, while liquids heavier than water have API gravities below 10. The relation between API gravity and specific gravity is shown by the following formula:

$$\text{API Gravity (degrees)} = \frac{141.5}{\text{Sp Gr at 60 F}} - 131.5$$

---

* 1916 Race St., Philadelphia 3, Penna.

Table 3—Limiting Requirements for Diesel Fuel Oils[a]
ASTM Designation: D 975

(Consult ASTM Headquarters for Complete and Latest Specifications)

Grade of Diesel Fuel Oil	Flash Point, deg. Fahr.	Pour Point, deg. Fahr.	Water and Sediment, per cent by volume	Carbon Residue on 10 per cent Residuum, per cent	Ash per cent by weight	Distillation Temperatures, deg. Fahr.		Viscosity at 100 F.		Sulfur, per cent by weight	Copper Strip Corrosion	Cetane Number[d]
						90 per cent Point	End Point	Kinematic, centistokes (or Saybolt Universal, sec.)				
	Min.	Max.	Max.	Max.	Max.	Max.	Max.	Min.	Max.	Max.	Max.	Min.
No. 1-D {A volatile distillate fuel oil for engines in service requiring frequent speed and load changes.	100 or legal	....[b]	Trace	0.15	0.01	....	625	1.4	....	0.50	No. 3	40[c]
No. 2-D {A distillate fuel oil of lower volatility for engines in industrial and heavy mobile service.	125 or legal	....[b]	0.10	0.35	0.02	675	....	1.8 (32.0)	5.8 (45)	1.0	No. 3	40[c]
No. 4-D {A fuel oil for low and medium speed engines.	130 or legal	....[b]	0.50	....	0.10	....	....	5.8 (45)	26.4 (125)	2.0	....	30[c]

a To meet special operating conditions, modifications of individual limiting requirements may be agreed upon between purchaser, seller, and supplier.

b For cold weather operation the pour point should be specified 10 F below the ambient temperature at which the engine is to be operated except where fuel oil heating facilities are provided.

c Low-atmospheric temperatures as well as engine operation at high altitudes may require use of fuels with higher cetane ratings.

d Where cetane number is not available Calculated Cetane Index from Fig. 33 page 108 may be used as an approximation.

GRADE No. 1-D comprises the class of volatile fuel oils from kerosene to the intermediate distillates. Fuels within this classification are applicable for use in high-speed engines in services involving frequent and relatively wide variations in loads and speeds, and also for use in cases where abnormally low fuel temperatures are encountered.

GRADE No. 2-D includes the class of distillate gas oils of lower volatility. These fuels are applicable for use in high-speed engines in services involving relatively high loads and uniform speeds, or in engines not requiring fuels having the higher volatility or other properties specified for Grade No. 1-D.

GRADE No. 4-D covers the class of more viscous distillates and blends of these distillates with residual fuel oils. These fuels are applicable for use in low- and medium-speed engines employed in services involving sustained loads at substantially constant speed.

Reprinted by permission of the American Society for Testing Materials.

Table 4—Detailed Requirements for Fuel Oils.[a]
ASTM Designation: D 396

(Consult ASTM Headquarters for Complete and Latest Specifications)

Grade of Fuel Oil[b]	Flash Point, deg Fahr, Min.	Pour Point, deg Fahr, Max.	Water and Sediment, per cent by volume, Max.	Carbon Residue on 10 per cent Bottoms, per cent, Max.	Ash, per cent by weight, Max.	Distillation Temperatures, deg Fahr — 10 per cent Point, Max.	90 per cent Point, Max.	End Point, Max.	Saybolt Viscosity, sec — Universal At 100 F, Max.	Universal At 100 F, Min.	Furol At 122 F, Max.	Furol At 122 F, Min.	Kinematic Viscosity, centistokes — At 100 F, Max.	At 100 F, Min.	At 122 F, Max.	At 122 F, Min.	Gravity, deg API, Min.	Copper Strip Corrosion, Max.
No. 1 — A distillate oil intended for vaporizing pot-type burners and other burners requiring this grade of fuel	100 or legal	0	trace	0.15	……	420	……	625	……	……	……	……	2.2	1.4	……	……	35	No. 3
No. 2 — A distillate oil for general purpose domestic heating for use in burners not requiring No. 1 fuel oil	100 or legal	20[c]	0.10	0.35	……	d	675	……	40	……	……	……	(4.3)	……	……	……	26	……
No. 4 — An oil for burner installations not equipped with preheating facilities	130 or legal	20	0.50	……	0.10	……	……	……	125	45	……	……	(26.4)	(5.8)	……	……	……	……
No. 5 — A residual-type oil for burner installations equipped with preheating facilities	130 or legal	……	1.00	……	0.10	……	……	……	……	150	40	……	……	(32.1)	(81)	……	……	……
No. 6 — An oil for use in burners equipped with preheaters permitting a high-viscosity fuel	150	……	2.00[e]	……	……	……	……	……	……	……	300	45	……	……	(638)	(92)	……	……

a Recognizing the necessity for low-sulfur fuel oils used in connection with heat-treatment, non-ferrous metal, glass, and ceramic furnaces and other special uses, a sulfur requirement may be specified in accordance with the following table:

Grade of Fuel Oil	Sulfur, max, per cent
No. 1	0.5
No. 2	1.0
No. 4	no limit
No. 5	no limit
No. 6	no limit

Other sulfur limits may be specified only by mutual agreement between the purchaser and the seller.

b It is the intent of these classifications that failure to meet any requirement of a given grade does not automatically place an oil in the next lower grade unless in fact it meets all requirements of the lower grade. However, these specifications shall not require a pour point lower than 0 F under any conditions.

c Lower or higher pour points may be specified whenever required by conditions of storage or use.

d The 10 per cent point may be specified at 440 F maximum for use in other than atomizing burners.

e The amount of water by distillation plus the sediment by extraction shall not exceed 2.00 per cent. The amount of sediment by extraction shall not exceed 0.50 per cent. A deduction shall be made for all water and sediment in excess of 1.0 per cent.

Reprinted by permission of the American Society for Testing Materials.

It is important to note that lighter liquids have lower specific gravities and higher API gravities than heavier liquids.

Gravity also varies with the temperature of a liquid, so that both methods are expressed in terms of a given temperature. In the United States this temperature is 60 F.

In so far as Diesel fuels are concerned, gravity, however measured, can be correlated closely with heat content, as will be explained below. If other characteristics, such as boiling range, are known, gravity is also an indication of fuel composition and can be related by cetane number. This relation will be discussed at a later point.

The API gravity of a *residual* fuel may vary from –3 to 18 for a No. 6 fuel* and from 0 to 24.8 for a No. 5 fuel. Gravity cannot be correlated with viscosity. It is desirable to select a fuel that is lighter than water to facilitate centrifuging. It is also better to use the lighter grades of *residuals;* however, a low gravity fuel of low viscosity could be a good fuel providing other attributes are satisfactory. As a general rule, however, the heavier fuels are those that have been cracked further with the result that they are more viscous and have a higher carbon content.

Flash Point (ASTM D 92, ASA Z11.6).—The flash point of a fuel is that temperature at which an open flame introduced above the fuel surface will cause ignition of the fuel vapors, under standard test conditions. Flash point bears no relation to fuel performance in the engines, but is important from the standpoint of insurance, fire laws, and transportation regulations. While these rules are not uniform, a minimum flash point of 150 F is usually sufficient to meet them. This requirement is normally met by all but the lightest grades of Diesel fuel.

Water and Sediment (ASTM D 96).—Cleanliness is often considered the most important item in Diesel fuel specifications. Contamination in the form of abrasives, water, and gummy constituents is very harmful if present in quantities over a trace. Cleanliness after delivery is largely a matter of handling, condition of tanks and fuel lines, and servicing of filters and strainers. Excessive water may separate and reach the nozzles in quantities sufficient to cause misfiring and to accelerate corrosion with possible seizing of fuel pumps and injectors. The action of abrasive and gummy material is well known.

The cleanliness of a fuel is determined by centrifuging a 50-50 mixture of fuel and benzol and measuring the amount of material separated from the mixture. The maximum amount of water and sediment, often expressed as BS&W (bottom sediment and water)

---

* From Bureau of Mines Information Circular 7762, Aug., 1956, "National Survey of Burner Fuel Oils, 1956."

for an ASTM 2-D fuel, is limited to 0.1 percent maximum. This fuel is commonly used in medium speed engines. According to the ASTM D 396 specification, water and sediment for *residual* fuels is limited to 2 percent for No. 6 fuel with the amount of sediment by extraction not exceeding 0.5 percent. For No. 5 fuel the water and sediment is limited to 1 percent. To establish any specified limits below this standard would mean premium fuel prices. In selecting fuels for use in Diesel engines, selection of those fuels that contain a minimum of BS&W will lighten the work that the centrifuges have to do, as well as reduce their maintenance.

Viscosity (ASTM D 88, D 445, D 446; ASA Z11.2, Z11.46). —Viscosity is a measure of resistance to flow, and hence indicates facility of transfer and injection characteristics. High viscosity (thick) oils cannot be pumped easily unless the viscosity is reduced by heating. Viscosity limits in this respect vary with installation details; however, fuels having a viscosity of less than 150 SSU at 100 F are generally satisfactory without heating. Viscosity also affects injection characteristics, high viscosity fuels tending to give a coarse, high penetration spray rather than a finely atomized one. Here again, different engine models vary considerably in their requirements, small, high speed units being the most critical. If a fuel is too high in viscosity, this can be reduced by preheating the fuel, and thus it may be satisfactory provided it is properly handled.

In connection with *residual* fuels the ASTM specification D 396 has established viscosity limitations for No. 6 fuels at from 45 to 300 SSF at 122 F and for No. 5 fuels at from 40 SSF at 122 F to 150 SSU at 100 F. When used for Diesel fuel, the less viscous ones should be selected, if available, as lower temperatures and less heat are required to bring them down to suitable operating viscosities. See Viscosity-Temperature Chart, Fig. 32, page 97.

Carbon Residue (ASTM D 189, ASA Z11.25).—Carbon residue, sometimes called Conradson Carbon, gives a measure of the carbon depositing tendencies of a fuel oil when heated in a bulb under prescribed conditions. While not directly correlating with engine deposits, this property is considered an approximation. It is expressed as a percentage, by weight, of the original sample. In the case of light fuels, where such deposits would normally be exceedingly small, the test is run on the 10 percent remaining after the lightest 90 percent of the fuel has been distilled off. This test is referred to as "Carbon Residue on 10 percent bottoms," and gives values in the range of 10 or more times those obtained when the test is run on the entire fuel.

Both carbon residue tests are believed to indicate the approximate carbon forming tendencies of the fuels when burned in Diesel engines; however, the results do not correlate exactly with engine test results. Recently there has been a trend toward replacing the

Conradson Carbon Residue test with the more expedient Ramsbottom Test (ASTM D 524, ASA Z11.47).

There is no established limit for carbon residue in a *residual* fuel. The percentage in a fuel depends on several factors—the crude source, refining process, how far the residual has been cracked, etc. Carbon residue can vary from 1 percent to 18 percent, or even more. Carbon residue in the lower concentrations affects the operation of a Diesel very little. Higher concentrations may, under some conditions, cause a smoky exhaust. Specific fuel consumption may be affected by the presence of excessive carbon residue.

Ash Content (ASTM D 482, ASA Z11.54).—The ash content of a fuel is measured by burning a sample in a crucible under high temperature, so that only the incombustible components remain. Such components are undesirable because they may reflect the presence of abrasive materials. A high ash content may also indicate the presence of material in solution in the fuel that, though not abrasive, may cause trouble by forming incrustations on the injector tips, which may interfere with fuel spray. For this reason, ash content should be held to a low value, preferably less than 0.02 percent for higher speed engines and less than 0.1 percent for low speed engines.

For *residual* fuels the percentage of ash after centrifuging is a figure that is subject to wide variation. If the centrifuging has been efficient the remaining ash is soluble ash and little can be done economically to reduce it. It is reasonable to expect an ash in the fuel after centrifuging of from .01 to .05 percent.

Cloud and Pour Point (ASTM D 97, ASA Z11.7)—The cloud point is the temperature at which the fuel becomes cloudy, as the result of the formation of wax crystals. The pour point of a fuel is that temperature at which it will cease to flow, as measured under standard conditions.

The cloud point is not important as regards flow of fuel to the pump at low temperatures; however, it may be important in connection with clogging of fuel filters.

Pour point may be important, depending on other fuel characteristics, in governing whether or not the fuel can be pumped under low temperature conditions. However, it should be remembered that the pour point temperature is determined in a small jar, rather than in a large tank, and that the viscosity of the fuel at low temperatures may be of equal or greater importance than pour point.

Where requirements for low cloud and pour points may lead to increased fuel cost, provision of heating equipment in the fuel handling system may be worthwhile in eliminating handling difficulties on the lower-cost fuel.

Sulfur.—Sulfur, in burning, changes to oxides which in themselves are quite free from corrosive effect. The corrosive effect attributed to sulfur is due to the formation of sulfuric or sulfurous acid. These acids are produced by a chemical reaction of the oxides and the water of combustion. They are harmful when their condensation occurs on critical engine parts. It is well, in selecting fuels, to choose those that have low sulfur content. Harmful effects of high sulfur fuel can sometimes be reduced by the use of heavy-duty lubricating oils designed for such purpose and by operating at higher jacket water temperatures to prevent condensation.

Corrosion (ASTM D 130, ASA Z11.21).—Corrosion is usually measured by immersing a polished copper strip in the fuel for a period of three hours at 212 F. This test is chiefly of value in predicting the corrosion to be expected in copper fuel lines and brass fuel strainers used on many engines. It does not appear to correlate with corrosion of fuel injectors or other engine parts.

Ignition Quality (ASTM D 613).—Fuel oils do not ignite immediately after being injected into the combustion chamber of a Diesel engine. The interval of time which elapses between the time injection begins and the time ignition starts varies widely for different fuel oils, when injected into the same combustion chamber and under the same conditions of pressure, temperature and other operating conditions. Ignition quality is defined as the relative rapidity with which the start of ignition follows the beginning of injection for various fuel oils. The accepted measure for comparing ignition quality is the cetane number.

The cetane number of a Diesel fuel is the whole number nearest the percentage by volume of normal cetane in a blend of normal cetane and alpha-methylnaphthalene that matches the ignition quality of the fuel in question. Cetane is a hydrocarbon with a high and very constant ignition quality. Alpha-methylnaphthalene is a hydrocarbon with very poor ignition quality. A fuel oil with an ignition quality which matches that of a blend consisting of 40 percent cetane and 60 percent alpha-methylnaphthalene would have a cetane number of 40.

The cetane number of a Diesel fuel oil is determined by testing it in a standard test engine under standard test conditions, and varying the compression ratio until the delay period between the beginning of injection and ignition is a fixed amount (13 deg.), all other operating conditions such as rpm, timing of injection, quantity of injection, temperatures, etc., remaining constant and standard for this test. When this compression ratio has been determined, the cetane number is the whole number nearest the percentage of cetane in a blend of cetane and alpha-methylnaphthalene which has the same delay period at the same compression ratio in the standard test engine.

The ignition quality of a Diesel fuel oil is important as it has a marked effect on the operation of the engine, and its importance increases as the engine speed increases. If the ignition quality of the fuel is low, a large part of the fuel charge is injected into the combustion chamber before ignition occurs. When ignition occurs it spreads rapidly through the fuel already present in the combustion chamber, resulting in rapid increase in pressure and often detonation. For lower speed engines with larger bores and strokes, more time is available for ignition and combustion, and Diesel fuel oils having poorer ignition qualities (lower cetane numbers) are satisfactory. For higher speed engines of smaller bores and strokes, fuel oils having better ignition qualities (higher cetane numbers) are required.

The use of a fuel oil with too low a cetane number for a given engine results in rough operation, higher fuel consumption, smoky exhaust, etc. Starting may be more difficult. The cetane number of the fuel has an effect on the engine warm-up period. If an engine is to be operated in low temperature conditions for prolonged periods at light loads, or where fast warm-up is required, the cetane number of the fuel should be chosen high enough to avoid misfiring. The use of Diesel fuel oils having a cetane number higher than that required by a given engine may result in increased fuel cost with little or no improvement in operation.

Several empirical methods have been developed by which the approximate cetane number or the ignition quality can be calculated from laboratory data, such as gravity, viscosity, volatility, and analine cloud point. These methods should be used with caution as they are subject to many limitations, and although values determined by these methods may be of some value if the actual cetane number is not available, they cannot be substituted for the cetane numbers, as determined in a test engine. These empirical methods are not applicable to fuels containing additives for raising the cetane number, to pure hydrocarbons or fuels produced by certain processes.

The Diesel index number based on the API gravity and the analine cloud point, the most widely use of these methods in the past, is so much less accurate than the cetane number that it is no longer recommended.

The most useful of the empirical methods is the one developed by the Coordinating Research Council, a description of which appears in the ASTM Standards on Fuels and Lubricants (D 975). The value determined by this method is known as the "Calculated Cetane Index." The calculated cetane index number corresponds very closely with the ASTM cetane number for distillate fuel oils having a cetane number within the range of 30 to 60, the variation being in the order of plus or minus two cetane numbers. This method is not applicable to fuels containing additives for increasing the cetane number, to pure hydrocarbons, synthetic fuels, alkylates or coal tar products. Substantial inaccuracies may occur if used for crude oil, residuals, or products having a volatility of below 500 F end point. It is particularly applicable to straight-run fuels, catalytically-cracked stocks, and blends of the two.

To obtain the calculated cetane index of a fuel oil, it is necessary to know the API gravity and to have an accurate determination of the mid-boiling point temperature (F) for 50 percent recovery— ASTM distillation. Having this information, the calculated cetane index number is found from the alignment chart, Fig. 33, reprinted by permission of the American Society for Testing Materials.

Volatility and Distillation Range (ASTM D 158, ASA Z11.26).—The volatility of a fuel refers to its vaporizing tendencies when distilled at atmospheric pressure under standard conditions. It is usually expressed in terms of the distillation range, giving the temperatures at which successive 10 percent increments of the fuel are distilled, condensed and collected in a graduate. The temperature for the first 10 percent distilled for medium Diesel fuels will range from 400 F to 480 F. Most No. 1 fuels will generally run lower. While this factor may not in itself be especially significant, it is contributory to the overall volatility characteristics of the fuel which do influence engine performance. The 90 percent distillation point for lighter fuels is important and is usually set to a maximum of 675 F. In the case of low speed engines, higher values may be permitted.

The higher percentage distillation points are an indication of the combustibility of the fuel. In heavier fuels the end point may be less than 90 percent.

Heat Value (ASTM D 240, ASA Z11.14).—Performance guarantees are usually expressed in terms of a specified heat value of the fuel; accordingly some fuel contracts are also written in terms of this factor.

The unit used in expressing heat value is the Btu, or British Thermal Unit, which is the amount of heat required to raise the temperature of a pound of water one degree F, under specified conditions.

Heat value of fuels may be given in either of two ways: high heat value or low heat value. Both values are determined by burning the fuel in a calorimeter, measuring the amount of heat actually released by a known quantity of fuel. The high heat value includes the heat liberated by condensation of the water formed by combustion of the fuel, while the low heat value does not.

All heat engines utilize only the low heat of whatever fuel is used. The high heat value of fuels containing hydrogen includes some heat not available for conversion into work in any internal combustion engine. Due to the greater ease and accuracy with which the high heat value of fuel oil can be determined, oil refiners and distributors sell oil on the high heat basis exclusively. Furthermore, the difference between high and low heat values of fuel oils is a fairly constant percentage. It is for this reason fuel oil consumption guarantees are based on the high heat value.

FIG. 33. CALCULATED CETANE INDEX

BASED ON EQUATION:

CALCULATED CETANE INDEX = 97.833 (LOG MID B PT, *°F)^2 + 2.2088 (API) (LOG MID B PT, °F) + 0.01247 (API)^2 − 423.51 (LOG MID B PT, °F) − 4.7808 (API) + 419.59

*TEMPERATURE FOR 50% RECOVERED AT 760 MM HG BAROMETRIC PRESSURE

CORRECTION FOR BAROMETRIC PRESSURE

MID B PT °F TEMP RANGE	CORRECTION[1] FOR EACH 10 MM DIFF IN PRESSURE
374 - 410	1.02
410 - 446	1.06
446 - 482	1.11
482 - 518	1.15
518 - 554	1.19
554 - 590	1.24
590 - 626	1.28
626 - 662	1.32
662 - 698	1.37

[1]TO BE ADDED FOR PRESSURES BELOW 760 MM HG, OR SUBTRACTED FOR PRESSURES ABOVE 760 MM HG

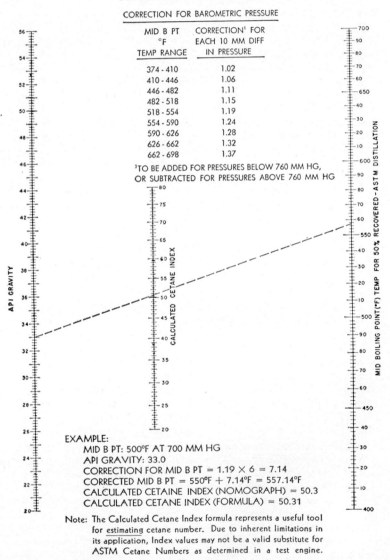

EXAMPLE:
MID B PT: 500°F AT 700 MM HG
API GRAVITY: 33.0
CORRECTION FOR MID B PT = 1.19 × 6 = 7.14
CORRECTED MID B PT = 550°F + 7.14°F = 557.14°F
CALCULATED CETAINE INDEX (NOMOGRAPH) = 50.3
CALCULATED CETANE INDEX (FORMULA) = 50.31

Note: The Calculated Cetane Index formula represents a useful tool for estimating cetane number. Due to inherent limitations in its application, Index values may not be a valid substitute for ASTM Cetane Numbers as determined in a test engine.

Reprinted by permission of the American Society for Testing Materials.

Table 5—High and Low Heating Values of Some Typical Diesel Fuels*

Gravity, °API	Sp. Gravity, at 60 F	Weight Fuel, lbs/gallon	High Heating Value		Low Heating Value	
			Btu/lb	Btu/gallon	Btu/lb	Btu/gallon
44	0.8063	6.713	19,860	133,500	18,600	125,000
42	0.8155	6.790	19,810	134,700	18,560	126,200
40	0.8251	6.870	19,750	135,800	18,510	127,300
38	0.8348	6.951	19,680	137,000	18,460	128,500
36	0.8448	7.034	19,620	138,200	18,410	129,700
34	0.8550	7.119	19,560	139,400	18,360	130,900
32	0.8654	7.206	19,490	140,600	18,310	132,100
30	0.8762	7.296	19,420	141,800	18,250	133,300
28	0.8871	7.387	19,350	143,100	18,190	134,600
26	0.8984	7.481	19,270	144,300	18,130	135,800
24	0.9100	7.578	19,190	145,600	18,070	137,100
22	0.9218	7.676	19,110	146,800	18,000	138,300
20	0.9340	7.778	19,020	148,100	17,930	139,630
18	0.9465	7.882	18,930	149,400	17,860	140,900
16	0.9593	7.989	18,840	150,700	17,790	142,300
14	0.9725	8.099	18,740	152,000	17,710	143,600
12	0.9861	8.212	18,640	153,300	17,620	144,900
10	1.000	8.328	18,540	154,600	17,540	146,200

Note: It should be understood that heating values for a given gravity of fuel oil may vary somewhat from those shown in the above table.
*Bureau of Standards, Miscellaneous Publication No. 97; Thermal Properties of Petroleum Products, April 28, 1933.

In the case of petroleum fuels, as mentioned above, heat content may be calculated approximately from either the specific or API gravity. Table 5 shows the relation between specific gravity, API gravity, pounds per gallon, and high and low heat value in terms of both Btu per pound and Btu per gallon for the general run of petroleum fuels.

It will be noticed that, while the high API gravity fuels have the highest Btu per pound, they have the lowest Btu per gallon. Since fuels are usually purchased on a volume basis, the greater Btu content per gallon of the low gravity fuels should be considered in calculating costs.

Acidity and Alkalinity.—Because of crude source and refining method, it is possible for fuel oils to be either acid or alkaline to the extent of causing difficulties of various types when used in engines, generally in the form of corrosion in tanks and storage lines. For this reason, the fuel should be nearly neutral, and free from either acidity or alkalinity. In the case of light fuels, the crudes and processes used almost automatically assure a neutral product, to the extent that acidity and alkalinity tests are not normally specified. For heavier fuels, such a test is desirable in many instances.

Color.—Generally speaking, the color of a fuel has no relation to engine performance, as a dark-colored or black fuel may give performance in the engine superior to that of a fuel golden in color and nearly transparent. However, excessive darkening of a light-colored fuel while in storage may be indicative of an unstable fuel which may have tendency to form gummy or tarry deposits.

Vanadium Compounds.—Vanadium compounds appear in most *residuals* to a greater or lesser extent. Vanadium pentoxide resulting from the combustion process has a corrosive effect on engine parts operating at temperatures in excess of 1200 F. In such cases vanadium of 70 ppm or vanadium pentoxide of 125 ppm should be considered the maximum. In choosing fuels for use in Diesel engines with parts operating above 1200 F, those containing minimum amounts of vanadium should be selected.

Fuel Additives.—There are additives available for use and sometimes incorporated by the refiner in No. 2 fuel oils for the purpose of inhibiting the formation of organic sediment or for dispersing sediment, or for both effects, and in some cases these also have anti-rusting properties. Another type of additive is sometimes used with No. 2 burner fuels to improve cetane number.

For heavier fuels additives are not in current use by refiners, although there are numerous additives on the market advertised to dissolve sludge, emulsify water, demulsify, improve combustion, reduce combustion deposits, lower pour point and/or reduce viscosity. Before any of these are used, the recommendations of the fuel supplier should be obtained.

Engine Variations.—It is not possible to formulate tables or charts to show accurately the minimum cetane number, maximum carbon content, etc., against a size or speed coordinate, such as cylinder bore or revolutions per minute. If all Diesel engines were made to one basic design, such a correlation might be made; but the situation is quite the reverse. There are variations between single- and multi-orifice fuel nozzles, direct injection into the combustion space and injection into a pre-combustion chamber, high air turbulence and comparative quiescence. Each system has its particular advantages that affect fuel limitations.

Fuel Selection.—As mentioned previously, the engine manufacturer's recommendations are the logical starting point in selecting a fuel. In addition, the ASTM specifications, shown in Tables 3 and 4, will be found helpful. However, both types of specifications usually permit some latitude, which may be employed to effect operating economies by the use of less expensive fuels. This is particularly true in the case of large engines. The effect of fuel specifications on operating economies varies considerably, but may be briefly summarized as follows:

1. Extremely restrictive specifications generally increase fuel price by restricting refinery flexibility, or by requiring additional processing.

2. Increasing cetane number above the minimum required for smooth running does not increase operating efficiency, but may increase fuel cost.

3. Use of lighter fuels than actually required increases fuel cost per barrel and also increases fuel consumption because of decreased heat content per barrel.

4. In large engines the use of heavy residual fuels has been found economical in many cases. In other cases, operating difficulties may offset the low cost of the fuel. In general, successful operation on this type of fuel requires (a) selected residual fuels, (b) adequate purification and heating before use, and (c) more careful attention to overall operation.

Aerial view of Carthage, Missouri, Water and Electric Plant with six two-cycle dual fuel engines ranging from 2250 to 5900 hp.

CHAPTER THIRTEEN

Gaseous Fuels

Gaseous fuels used in internal combustion engines come from many sources and vary widely in their chemical composition and heating value. Even gases originating from the same source may vary continually in these characteristics. The temperature and the pressure at which they are delivered to the installation may also vary. Gaseous fuels may be free of water vapor, saturated with water vapor or, as is usually the case, may contain an amount of water vapor between these limits.

It should be noted here that the term "dry gas," as used by the gas industry, does not refer to water or water vapor but means gas free from hydrocarbon liquids. In order to prevent confusion in this matter, the same practice is followed by the internal combustion engine industry. Gaseous fuels used in the internal combustion industry are usually free from liquid hydrocarbons or "dry." If this is not the case, special agreement should be made between the engine builder and the buyer as to proper treatment of the wet gas to insure satisfactory engine performance.

Gaseous fuels are measured in cubic feet but, owing to the above variations, fuel consumption guarantees are always expressed on a basis of Btu, low heating value (lhv), actually used by the engine. This practice makes it possible for the engine builder to state performance guarantees regardless of the chemical composition, heating value, temperature, pressure or the water vapor content of the fuel gas.

The reasons for always using low heating value (lhv) in stating or guaranteeing fuel consumptions in connection with engines using gaseous fuels are as follows:

(1) The gas engine, like all other prime movers, can only convert into power the heat energy represented by the Btu (lhv) actually delivered to the engine.

(2) Due to the continual variation between the Btu (lhv) and the Btu (hhv) of all common gaseous fuels, guarantees are meaningless if based on the high heat value.

(3) Guarantees made on a basis of Btu (lhv) of any given gas as delivered to the engine will be correct regardless of any variation in the composition of the gas fuel supplied.

(4) Accurate information regarding the chemical composition, temperature, pressure and amount of water vapor in the fuel as delivered to the engine is never available at the time of bidding.

The importance of this practice of using the low heating value for gaseous fuel consumption guarantees is understood when the wide and continued variation which can exist between the high and the low heating values of commercial gaseous fuels is realized. The reason for this wide and continually changing variation between the high and the low heating values of commercial gases is because all these gases are composed of a continually changing mixture of a number of elementary gases each one having a different relation between its high and its low heating value. In addition, there are present various amounts of non-combustible gases and water vapor which have no heating value.

A gaseous fuel, for example, composed entirely of carbon monoxide, which produces no water vapor by its combustion, has the same high and low heating value. On the other hand, if the fuel was composed entirely of hydrogen, which produces only water vapor by its combustion, there would be a difference between the high heating value (325 Btu) and the low heating (275 Btu) amounting to 50 Btu or 18.2%. The gas engine, like all other prime movers, can only convert into work the heat energy represented by the low heating value of the gaseous fuel. Thus the specific fuel consumption if based on the high heating value would be 18.2% higher for the same engine when using hydrogen for fuel as when using carbon monoxide. If the comparison is made on a basis of the low heating value of the fuels, the fuel consumption would be the same in both cases.

The two gases used in the above example represent the extreme limits in the difference in the high and the low heating value of gases. All commercially available gases used for fuel in internal combustion engines are composed of mixtures of one or both of the above gases, numerous hydrocarbon gases such as CH_4, C_2H_4, C_xH_y, neutral gases such as N_2 and CO_2, and sometimes small percentages of sulphur and phosphorous compounds. Of the above gases the hydrocarbons are the only ones which have a different high and low heating value. The difference between the high and the low heating value of any of these hydrocarbons is always less than that of hydrogen but more than that of carbon monoxide. This difference will never be 18.2% but differences of 10% are common.

Gaseous fuels are delivered to the engine at various pressures and temperatures and in order to determine fuel consumption, the low heat value, as well as the pressure and temperature must be known. Gas heat values shall be based on saturated gas. Where greatest accuracy of test results is required, corrections may be applied to gas-volume measurements to adjust for the actual water-vapor content in the gas used for testing. In such cases the water content may be determined by Dew Point method (See ASTM D1142, ASA Z77.3) and the Calorific Value converted as described in Section 19 of ASTM D900. It must be understood that this equipment is costly and the operation thereof to assure accurate and reliable values requires special treatment. The pressure of the gaseous fuel at the meter is determined by a mercury column or by a calibrated pressure gage if the pressure is beyond the range of a mercury column. The temperature is determined by an accurate thermometer or by a thermo-couple properly located in the gas main at the meter.

The low heat value of saturated gas (or the chemical composition from which the heat value may be calculated) is generally available from the company supplying the gas. Composition of the gas and the heat value should be confirmed by submitting a gas sample to a reputable laboratory for analysis, bearing in mind that such analyses will not show the humidity of the gas entering the engine which may have an effect on the Btu content.

Gaseous fuel consumption in cubic feet shall be determined preferably by means of an orifice meter. The orifice meter is preferred since the condition of this type of meter can be easily checked in the field and is therefore more reliable. Construction and installation specifications of orifice meters and factors for determining the flow of gas through orifice meters as given in the A.G.A.* Gas Measurement Committee Report No. 3, "Orifice Metering of Natural Gas," (Current Edition) are used in orifice metering of natural gases.

Gaseous fuel consumption may also be found by means of other types of meters, such as venturi or by means of positive displacement type meters if calibrated immediately before and after test. Holder drop method may also be used.

The measurement of gas by an orifice meter in accordance with A.G.A. Report No. 3 is primarily for natural gas. When applied to other than natural gas the possibility of a slight error exists, but results are sufficiently accurate for all practical purposes. For this reason one of the other methods for measuring gases is recommended only if extremely accurate results are required.

Regardless of the type of meter used the results obtained are only acceptable if the flow rate is within the limits of the particular type of meter.

If by special agreement a calorimeter is used and the dew point is determined at the installation, the Btu (lhv) per cu ft of the gas as metered is best determined by a Junkers type calorimeter. In case it is operated at the same pressure and temperature as exists at the engine meter, and if the gas at the engine meter is saturated, no correction is necessary, because the Junkers type of calorimeter gives the Btu (lhv) per cu ft of the gas saturated with water vapor. If the gas as metered is not saturated a correction must be made to the Btu (lhv) per cu ft as shown by the calorimeter to give the Btu (lhv) per cu ft of the gas as metered as follows:

Btu (lhv) per cu ft of gaseous fuel as metered $= F_m$

$$F_m = F_x \times \frac{p_m - p_{mw}}{p_x - p_{xw}}$$

---

* American Gas Association, 420 Lexington Ave., New York 17, N. Y.

Where $F_x =$ Btu per cu ft of saturated gas at calorimeter
$p_m =$ absolute total pressure at engine meter, psia
$p_{mw} =$ absolute partial pressure of water vapor at engine meter,[1] psia
$p_x =$ absolute total pressure at calorimeter, psia
$p_{xw} =$ absolute partial pressure of water vapor at temperature of gas at calorimeter,[2] psia.

If the heating value of the gaseous fuel [Btu (lhv) per cu ft] is obtained at some other conditions of pressure, temperature and

Table 6—Vapor Pressure of Water[3]

Temp., deg F	Abs. press., psia	Temp., deg F	Abs. press., psia	Temp., deg F	Abs. press., psia	Temp., deg F	Abs. press., psia
32	0.08854	55	0.2141	77	0.4593	99	0.9210
33	0.09223	56	0.2220	78	0.4747	100	0.9492
34	0.09603	57	0.2302	79	0.4906	101	0.9781
35	0.09995	58	0.2386	80	0.5069	102	1.0078
36	0.10401	59	0.2473	81	0.5237	103	1.0382
37	0.10821	60	0.2563	82	0.5410	104	1.0695
38	0.11256	61	0.2655	83	0.5588	105	1.1016
39	0.11705	62	0.2751	84	0.5771	106	1.1345
40	0.12170	63	0.2850	85	0.5959	107	1.1683
41	0.12652	64	0.2951	86	0.6152	108	1.2029
42	0.13150	65	0.3056	87	0.6351	109	1.2384
43	0.13665	66	0.3164	88	0.6556	110	1.2748
44	0.14199	67	0.3276	89	0.6766	111	1.3121
45	0.14752	68	0.3390	90	0.6982	112	1.3504
46	0.15323	69	0.3509	91	0.7204	113	1.3896
47	0.15914	70	0.3631	92	0.7432	114	1.4298
48	0.16525	71	0.3756	93	0.7666	115	1.4709
49	0.17157	72	0.3886	94	0.7906	116	1.5130
50	0.17811	73	0.4019	95	0.8153	117	1.5563
51	0.18486	74	0.4156	96	0.8407	118	1.6006
52	0.19182	75	0.4298	97	0.8668	119	1.6459
53	0.19900	76	0.4443	98	0.8935	120	1.6924
54	0.20642						

[1] The absolute partial pressure of the water vapor in the gaseous fuel as metered (p_{mw}) is the vapor pressure of water at the temperature at which the gaseous fuel is metered for the engine (which is taken from Table 6) multiplied by the relative humidity of the gaseous fuel at the meter. The relative humidity of the gaseous fuel is determined by the dew point method (See ASTM D 1142).

[2] If a Junkers type of calorimeter is used, the gas as metered to the calorimeter is saturated with water vapor and the absolute partial pressure of the water vapor (p_{xw}) is the vapor pressure of water at the temperature of the gaseous fuel as metered at the calorimeter. This partial pressure is found in Table 6.

[3] Reprinted, by permission, from Keenan and Keyes "Thermodynamic Properties of Steam," published by John Wiley and Sons, New York 16, N. Y.

humidity than that which exists at the gaseous fuel meter, then the Btu (lhv) per cu ft as found by the calorimeter must be corrected to give the Btu (lhv) per cu ft of the gaseous fuel as follows:

Btu (lhv) per cu ft gaseous fuel as metered $= F_m$

$$F_m = F_x \times \frac{t_x}{t_m} \times \frac{p_m - p_{mw}}{p_x - p_{xw}}$$

Where $F_x =$ Btu (lhv) per cu ft saturated gas at calorimeter
$t_x =$ absolute temperature of gas at calorimeter, deg F
$t_m =$ absolute temperature of gas at meter, deg F
$p_m =$ absolute total pressure of gas at meter, psia
$p_{mw} =$ absolute partial pressure of water vapor in gaseous fuel as metered, psia
$p_x =$ absolute total pressure of gas at calorimeter, psia
$p_{xw} =$ absolute partial pressure of water vapor at calorimeter inlet temperature, deg F.

The fuel consumption per kilowatt hour may now be determined directly from the foregoing as follows:

$$\text{Btu per kwhr, } q_b = \frac{F_m \times V_m}{P_e}$$

Where $F_m =$ Btu (lhv) per cu ft of gaseous fuel as metered
$V_m =$ Cu ft of gaseous fuel per hour as metered
$P_e =$ Net kilowatt hour output

and the

$$\text{Btu per net bhp-hr, } q_a = \frac{F_m \times V_m}{P_m}$$

Where $P_m =$ Net brake horsepower per hour output.

The fuel consumption in Btu per kwhr and in Btu per bhp-hr having been determined, the equivalent fuel consumption in cu ft of gas at standard conditions of 60 F, 30 inches of mercury (mercury at 32 F) and saturated with water vapor or at any other conditions specified, can be found as follows:

$$\text{Cu ft per kwhr, } v_b = \frac{q_b}{F_g}$$

Where $F_g =$ Btu (lhv) per cu ft of gaseous fuel at standard conditions or any other conditions specified

and the

$$\text{Cu ft per bhp-hr, } v_a = \frac{q_a}{F_g}.$$

Gaseous fuels come from many sources, as previously stated, and vary widely not only in their chemical composition but also in their

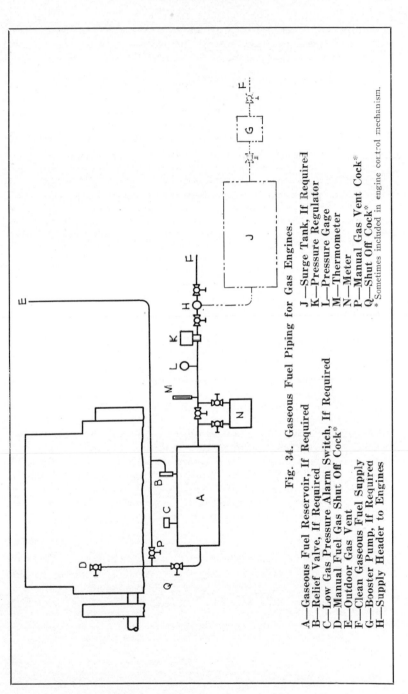

Fig. 34. Gaseous Fuel Piping for Gas Engines.

A—Gaseous Fuel Reservoir, If Required
B—Relief Valve, If Required
C—Low Gas Pressure Alarm Switch, If Required
D—Manual Fuel Gas Shut Off Cock*
E—Outdoor Gas Vent
F—Clean Gaseous Fuel Supply
G—Booster Pump, If Required
H—Supply Header to Engines

J —Surge Tank, If Required
K—Pressure Regulator
L—Pressure Gage
M—Thermometer
N—Meter
P—Manual Gas Vent Cock*
Q—Shut Off Cock*
*Sometimes included in engine control mechanism.

cleanliness. Many engines are located near main gas pipe lines or connected distributing systems and the gaseous fuel is obtained from these systems. This usually is clean, free from excessive amounts of water vapor and requires no treatment or cleaning before use in an engine. Other gases, such as sewage gases, are not clean and in addition may be saturated with water vapor. In such cases scrubbers and settling chambers must be installed in order to remove as much of these impurities and moisture as possible to make the gas suitable for use in the engine.

Sulphur and phosphorus are sometimes found in gaseous fuels. These gases or the products of the combustion of these gases may be corrosive especially if they come into contact with moisture. If any compounds of either are present precautions should be taken to keep the temperature of all parts of the engine and exhaust system that come into contact with these compounds above their dew point.

Complete information regarding the gaseous fuel to be used should be given to the engine manufacturer so that proper cleaning and handling equipment can be recommended.

In installations where the gas supply rate is variable, such as sewage disposal plants, gas holders are required. These should be of sufficient size to store any excess gas produced when the gas supply rate is higher than required by the engines and to deliver the gas during periods when the amount produced is lower than that required.

The gaseous fuel system (See Fig. 34) may be quite simple when the fuel supply is clean and of uniform quality, such as is the case in plants that take their gaseous fuel supply from a natural gas pipe line or distributing system, and only a gas meter and a pressure regulating valve are required. On the other hand, the system may be very complicated requiring, in addition to the above, reservoirs, valving, thermometers, gages, gas vent lines, relief valves, scrubbers and settling chambers. All vent lines should be carried outside the building and never connected to drains or sewers. In case the gas pressure is below the engine manufacturer's requirements, a booster compressor is necessary and an after cooler and oil separator may be required between the gas compressor and the engine.

Underwriters' Regulations.—The "Standards, No. 58, of the National Board of Fire Underwriters* for the Storage and Handling of Liquefied Petroleum Gases" should be scrupulously observed. Any local and state regulations governing such installations should also be investigated and observed. All reputable tank manufacturers are acquainted with these rules, and are accustomed, as a routine matter, to the construction of tanks which conform to them.

---

* 85 John St., New York 38, N. Y.

CHAPTER FOURTEEN

Generators and Electrical Equipment

A large number of stationary engine plants are engaged in the generation of electrical energy. It is therefore appropriate to include a chapter on this general subject. Comprehensive standards for electrical machinery have been developed and it is recommended that these be followed where they apply in the selection of engine driven electrical equipment. These standards are National Electrical Manufacturers Association Standards Publication No. MG1-1955, dated March 1955, entitled "Motors and Generators" and American Standards "Synchronous Generators, Synchronous Motors and Synchronous Machines in General," C50.1-1955, and "Direct-Current Generators, Direct-Current Motors, and Direct-Current Commutating Machines in General," C50.4-1955.

In the following text, when NEMA or American Standards are mentioned, reference is to the above publications or subsequent editions. The latest edition should, of course, be followed.

The electrical equipment involved in the production of power with Diesel engines consists essentially of the generators, either alternating or direct current, the exciters where required to furnish excitation current, and the switchboard for the control and distribution of the electric power.

Generators.—Although there are certain problems peculiar to the engine driven generator, the electrical characteristics do not differ fundamentally from generators driven by other types of prime movers. Generators are for either direct current or alternating current, as required. Standard voltages, temperature rises, speeds and other characteristics have been established in the American and NEMA Standards referred to above. Machinery conforming to such standards should be purchased whenever possible. Special voltages, temperature ratings, etc., can be obtained, but these tend to increase the cost and delay delivery of the equipment.

Generators for use with engines are rated at the load they are capable of carrying continuously without exceeding their temperature guarantees. The engine generator set rating should be the kw capacity normally available at the switchboard and corresponding to the full load rating of the generator and the engine, without imposing an overload on either the generator or the engine.

Temperature Ratings—Direct Current Generators. — Standard open-type direct current generators are normally rated with a 40 C temperature rise for continuous operation at rated load. These are based on an ambient temperature of 40 C and limited to elevations not exceeding 3300 feet.

There are cases where special enclosures may be necessary. In such cases the temperature rise of the machine is affected.

Enclosed machines can also be furnished for 40 C temperature rise but usually the cost is considerably higher than the more usual open type.

Tests for temperature rise, if required, should be made in accordance with American Standards and Test Codes.

Voltage, Kilowatt and Speed Ratings—Direct Current Generators.—(a) General Purpose Sizes—Generators rated ¾ kw at 3600 rpm up to and including generators having a continuous rating equivalent to 150 kw at 500 rpm (0.3 kw per rpm), open type but not exceeding 150 kw.

The standard voltages for general purpose direct current generators and exciters are 125 and 250 volts at full load.

The standard kilowatt and speed ratings of general purpose direct current generators and exciters vary with the type of drive, that is, belt-driven or coupled.

The standard kilowatt and speed ratings of general purpose belted direct current generators and belted exciters are as follows:

Kilowatt Ratings: 1, 1½, 2, 3, 5, 7½, 10, 15, 20, 25, 30, 40, 50, 60, 75, 100, 125 and 150 kw.

Speed Ratings: 1750, 1450, 1150, 850 and 575 rpm.

The standard kilowatt and speed ratings for general purpose coupled direct current generators and coupled exciters are as follows:

Kilowatt Ratings: ¾, 1, 1½, 2, 3, 5, 7½, 10, 15, 20, 25, 30, 40, 50, 60, 75, 100, 125 and 150 kw.

Speed ratings: 3600, 3000, 1800, 1500, 1200, 1000, 900, 750, 720, 600, 514, 500, 450, 428, 400, 375, 360, 333, 327, 300, 277, 273, 257, 250, 240, 231, 225, 214, 200, 188, 180, 167, 164, 150, 138, 136, 128, 125, 120, 115, 109, 107, 100, 94, 91, 90, 86, 83, 80, 79, and 75 rpm.

It is not practical to build all combinations of the above kilowatt and speed ratings. Consult NEMA Standards for ratings available.

(b) Direct Current Generators Larger Than General Purpose Sizes.

The standard voltages for direct current generators larger than general purpose sizes are 125, 250 and 600 volts at full load.

The standard kilowatt and speed ratings for direct current generators larger than general purpose sizes are as follows:

Kilowatt Ratings: 25, 30, 40, 50, 60, 75, 100, 125, 150, 175, 200, 250, 300, 350, 400, 500, 600, 700, 750, 800, 900, 1000, 1250, 1500, 1750, 2000, 2250, 2500, 3000, 3500, 4000, 4500 and 5000 kw.

The standard speed ratings conform to 60-cycle synchronous speeds as follows:

1200, 900, 720, 600, 514, 450, 400, 360, 327, 300, 277, 257, 240, 225, 200, 180, 164, 150, 138, 128, 120, 100, 90 and 80 rpm.

It is not practical to build all combinations of the above voltage, kilowatt and speed ratings. Consult NEMA Standards for ratings available.

Regulation—Direct Current Generators.—Due to the compound winding of direct current generators, and the ease with which the compounding can be varied within limits, voltage regulation does not offer any particular problem with this type of generator, except possibly where relatively large motors are to be started and any light flicker is considered objectionable. This can be minimized by the careful selection of motor starters, type of generator and auxiliary equipment. Automatic voltage regulators are frequently used with direct current generators to obtain improved voltage regulation, and better load distribution during parallel operation.

Parallel Operation—Direct Current Generators.—A direct current generator driven by an engine will operate in parallel with another generating unit, providing the governor characteristics of the various machines are similar and the generators are adjusted to have the same compounding so that they have approximately the same voltage characteristics.

Shunt-wound and stabilized-shunt-wound generators will operate successfully in parallel with other shunt-wound and stabilized-shunt-wound generators provided they also have drooping voltage characteristics. Compound-wound generators will operate successfully in parallel with each other provided they also are equipped with equalizing connections at the same polarity (normally on the negative side) and all generators have the same voltage drop at their respective rated loads from the point of connection of the equalizers through the series field to the bus bar. If it is necessary to install a resistance in the series field circuit to accomplish this result, such resistance should be furnished by the purchaser as a part of the station wiring. The resistance of the equalizer connection circuit between any two compound-wound generators should not exceed 20% of the resistance of the series field circuit of the smallest generator.

In ordering a generator where parallel operation is required, the complete details as well as the specifications of the existing machines should be given to the electrical equipment manufacturer.

Temperature Ratings—Synchronous Generators as Used with Engines.—Standard synchronous generators are rated at the load they are capable of carrying continuously without exceeding their temperature guarantees. This standard rating is expressed in kilovolt-amperes available at the terminals at 0.8 power factor. The corresponding kilowatt output should also be stated.

Ratings are normally on the basis of a 50 C temperature rise.

Temperature rises are based on an ambient temperature of 40 C and an altitude not exceeding 3300 feet (1000 meters).

Tests for temperature rise, if required, should be made in accordance with American Standards.

Voltage, Kilowatt and Speed Ratings.—Synchronous Generators.

—The standard voltage ratings are in accordance with American Standards. The standard kilowatt (Table 7) and speed ratings (Table 8) are in accordance with NEMA Standards.

Voltage Ratings. Standard voltage ratings for synchronous generators shall be:

120	4800; 5000[1]
120/208Y	6900
240	11500[2]
480	12500[2]
600	13800
2400; 2500[1]	14400
2400/4160Y; 2500/4330Y[1]	

Standard excitation voltages are 62.5, 125, 250, 375 and 500 volts direct current. However, those most commonly used for engine driven generators are 125 and 250 volts.

Table 7—Kilowatt Ratings

Standard kilowatt ratings at 0.8 power factor lagging

Kva	Kw	Kva	Kw	Kva	Kw
1.25	1	156	125	1875	1500
2.5	2	187	150	2188	1750
3.75	3	219	175	2500	2000
6.25	5	250	200	2812	2250
9.4	7.5	312	250	3125	2500
12.5	10	375	300	3750	3000
18.7	15	438	350	4375	3500
25	20	500	400	5000	4000
31.3	25	625	500	5625	4500
37.5	30	750	600	6250	5000
50	40	875	700	7500	6000
62.5	50	1000	800	8750	7000
75[3]	60[3]	1125	900	10000	8000
93.8	75	1250	1000	12500	10000
125	100	1563	1250	—	—

[1] The 2500, 2500/4330Y, and 5000 volt ratings are frequently desirable for serving nominal 2400, 2400/4160Y, and 4800 volt distribution systems.

[2] Recognized for use on established systems but not preferred for new undertakings.

[3] The standard speeds for this rating shall be 500 to 1800 rpm inclusive.

Speed Ratings. Standard synchronous speeds for U. S. applications correspond to 60 cycle frequencies. Speeds corresponding to 25 and 50 cycle frequencies are also available, particularly for foreign applications.

Table 8—Synchronous Speeds

No. of Poles	60 Cycle rpm	50 Cycle rpm	25 Cycle rpm
4	1800	1500	750
6	1200	1000	500
8	900	750	375
10	720	600	300
12	600	500	250
14	514	429	214
16	450	375	188
18	400	333	167
20	360	300	150
22	327	273	136
24	300	250	125
26	277	231	115
28	257	214	107
30	240	200	100
32	225	188	94
36	200	167	83
40	180	150	—
44	164	136	—
48	150	125	—
52	138	115	—
56	129	107	—
60	120	100	—
66	109	91	—
72	100	83	—
80	90	—	—
90	80	—	—

It is not practical to build all combinations of the above voltage, kilowatt and speed ratings.

Frequency Rating.—The standard U. S. frequency is 60 cycles. 25 and 50 cycles are used in some U. S. applications and in foreign countries.

Power Factor.—The standard power factor for synchronous generators is either unity or 0.8 lagging.

In the majority of cases 0.8 lagging power factor generators will be suitable. However, if special conditions require a lower power factor, machines of special design can be furnished at additional cost.

Allowable Variation from Rated Voltage.—American Standards specify that generators shall operate successfully at rated kva, frequency, and power factor, at any voltage not more than 5 percent above or below rated voltage but not necessarily in accordance with the standards of performance established for operation at rated voltage. However, self-regulated type generators are usually designed to operate at a single voltage except for variations caused by changes in load.

Ambient Temperature of Reference.—The standard ambient temperature is 40 C. In some applications, however, the ambient temperature may be 50 C. Generators designed for this higher value of ambient temperature are special.

Dielectric Test.—The standard test voltage for armature windings shall be an alternating voltage whose effective value is 1000 volts plus twice the rated voltage of the machine. Field windings of synchronous generators shall be tested with 10 times the exciter voltage but in no case with less than 1500 volts.

Parallel Operation of Synchronous Generators.—The generator manufacturer will furnish equipment with electrical characteristics suitable for parallel operation. Many of the factors which affect the parallel operation of generators are contained in the engine and the characteristics of the equipment connected to the system with which the generator must parallel also impose conditions which must be taken into account in parallel operation. Therefore the responsibility for coordinating this equipment rests with the engine builder. The generator manufacturer will furnish the engine builder with the value of synchronous coefficient P_r and the Wk^2 of the generator rotor.

In order to determine whether or not engine generator sets will operate satisfactorily in parallel, without resonance, it is necessary to investigate several factors which affect their operation. These factors are as follows:

1. The engine governors should have approximately the same characteristics and be in good mechanical condition.

2. The generators should be equipped with damper windings.

3. The Wk^2 of the individual units should be such that the natural frequencies of the combined units under all load conditions avoid the forced frequencies by a proper margin.

4. Voltage regulators should be provided with adequate cross-current compensation.

The first factor relates to the engine and has been discussed in Chapter Four. The second factor, having to do with damper windings, is taken care of in the manufacture of the generators. The third factor, the natural frequencies of the combined unit, applies to both the engine and generator in that the combined moment of inertia (Wk^2) of the unit is involved. The determination of the natural frequencies also requires a knowledge of the synchronizing coefficients (P_r) of the generator.

Synchronizing power is the power at synchronous speed corresponding to the torque developed at the air gap between the armature and field. This torque tends to restore the rotor to the no load position relative to the line voltage.

The synchronizing coefficient (P_r) is determined by dividing the shaft power by the corresponding angular displacement of the rotor. It is expressed in kilowatts (kw) per electrical radian. Unless otherwise stated, the values given will be for the steady state rated voltage, load, power factor and frequency.

Natural frequencies are calculated for both the no-load and maximum load conditions. The expression for the undamped natural frequency of oscillation on an infinite power system is as follows:

$$f_n = \frac{35,200}{n} \sqrt{\frac{P_r \times f}{Wk^2}}$$

Where $f_n =$ natural frequency in cycles per minute
$n =$ generator rated speed in rpm
$P_r =$ synchronizing coefficient (see above)
$f =$ frequency of circuit in cycles per second
$Wk^2 =$ total moment of inertia of rotating members.

Before the synchronizing coefficient P_r came into general use there were two other coefficients in use as follows:

P_o — stator kw output power divided by the corresponding angular displacement of the rotor in electrical radians
$P_s =$ stator kw output power divided by the corresponding angular displacement of the rotor in electrical degrees.

The approximate relation between these coefficients and the coefficient P_r is as follows:

$$P_r = 1.05\,P_o$$
$$P_r = 1.05 \times 57.3\,P_s$$

where 1.05 is the approximate relation between shaft power and electrical output; 57.3 is the number of electrical degrees in an electrical radian.

Wk^2 is the moment of inertia of the moving parts, and for the generator rotor, flywheel and other rotating masses is equal to the weight of the parts multiplied by the square of the radius of gyration of the parts, in feet. In an engine, however, it is necessary to refer the inertia of the reciprocating parts to a basis equivalent to that of the rotating parts.

The manufacturer of new equipment must have the following information on previously installed generating sets to permit the necessary design calculations for securing satisfactory parallel operation. This may involve adjustment of the Wk^2 of the new unit and in some cases may necessitate changes in the Wk^2 of the existing unit or units:

Engine

Manufacturer	2 or 4 Cycle
Model	Single or Double Acting
Serial No.	Engine Wk^2, lb-ft^2
No. of Cylinders	Flywheel Wk^2, lb-ft^2
Bore and Stroke	Make of Governor
Horsepower	Type of Governor
Speed, rpm	

Generator

Manufacturer	Cycles
Serial No.	Speed, rpm
Kva Rating	P_r
Voltage	Rotor Wk^2, lb-ft^2
Phase	Damper Windings, Yes or No.

Differences in the voltage characteristics of generators operating in parallel will not change the load distribution but will make the current generated by an individual unit lead or lag the current generated by others.

A hand or electrically operated synchronizing device (speed changer) is required for each unit to shift the load from one unit to another and thus divide the load proportionately in parallel operation. The operation of such a device will shift load without perceptibly changing speed. This synchronizing equipment is used also when an engine-generator unit is started up, to bring its speed to the speed of the loaded units before throwing the unit on the line in parallel.

See also Parallel Operation, page 29.

Torsional Vibration.—Since the factors which affect torsional vibration are contained principally in the design of the engine rather than in the design of the generator, the responsibility for avoiding torsional vibration troubles shall rest with the engine builder when combined units are sold. However, since the design of the generator rotor is an important factor which must be considered, the generator builder must give complete information concerning the generator design insofar as it affects torsional vibration.

The generator builder will furnish the engine builder with the moment of inertia (Wk^2) and weight of the generator and exciter rotors, shaft dimensions, and any other generator information as may affect the torsional calculations, in such detail as required by the engine manufacturer.

Before the generator spider and such part of the shaft as may be furnished by the generator builder are manufactured, the final draw ings of the same are to be submitted to the engine builder for approval insofar as their design affects torsional vibration.

See also Torsional Vibration, page 30 and Chapt. 5.

Overspeed Limitations.—Engine driven generators shall be so constructed that they will withstand without mechanical injury an overspeed of 25 percent.

Telephone Influence Factor.—Normally when telephone influence factor is specified, an engine driven synchronous generator shall have balanced TIF not exceeding the American Standards, as shown in Table 9.

Table 9—Telephone Influence Factor

Kva Rating of Generator	Balanced TIF
62.5 — 299	300
300 — 699	200
700 — 999	150
1000 — 2499	125
2500 — 9999	60

The residual component telephone influence factor of engine driven synchronous generators, having voltage ratings 2000 volts and higher, shall not exceed the following:

Kva Rating of Generator	Residual TIF
1000 — 2499	60
2499 — and above	30

Special consideration may be necessary where trouble exists or may be anticipated from difficult exposure conditions.

NOTE: Telephone influence factor of a synchronous generator is the measure of the possible effect of harmonics in the generator voltage wave on telephone circuits. TIF is measured at the generator terminals on open circuit at rated voltage and frequency.

Excitation.—Fields of engine driven generators may be excited in any of the following ways:

  1. A direct connected, belted or chain driven exciter is usually used.
  2. Self excitation
  3. From separate d-c source.

Regulation.—With a-c generators the voltage regulation is such that if full load is removed, the voltage, if not regulated, may rise to 140 percent of rated voltage. Such a generator would be said to have a 40 percent regulation. Load changes, whether instantaneous or gradual, will produce corresponding voltage changes that must be compensated for by adjustment of the excitation either directly by hand or automatically by a voltage regulator. Where load changes are gradual, or on a definite cycle, hand regulation of voltage is sometimes used, but automatic regulation is generally to be preferred.

On systems of moderate capacity, where it is necessary to start relatively large motors, reduced voltage motor-starting equipment is recommended to minimize voltage fluctuations. The starting current of a squirrel cage motor may be many times the full load current. If proper provision is not made, throwing such a load on a generator might cause an instantaneous voltage drop which, if too great, would cause low voltage releases to drop out.

Nameplates.—All generators should be provided with visible nameplates giving at least manufacturer's name, suitable identification, serial number and complete rating (voltage, kva output, power factor, time rating, temperature rise for rated continuous load, overload rating—if any—with corresponding temperature rise and time rating, rated speed in rpm, rated current in amperes per terminal, number of phases, frequency in cycles per second, rated exciter voltage, and rated field current).

General.—Amortisseur (damper) windings are recommended for all engine driven synchronous generators. Such windings are required for engine generator units which at the time of installation or at any future time are to operate in parallel.

Generators may be of the "engine type" in which case the generator shaft and all necessary bearings are furnished by the engine builder, or of the "coupled type" in which case the generator is furnished with a shaft and one or two bearings.

For further information regarding definitions, etc., refer to NEMA and American Standards.

Installation.—In the operation of generators it is important to supply them with clean air free from oil vapors, chemical fumes, abrasive dirt, dust, etc., so as to insure satisfactory life from the exposed wearing parts and insulated windings. It is also important to arrange the ventilation in the station so as to avoid subjecting the generators to an unusually high ambient temperature because of local recirculation of ventilating air or insufficient supply of fresh ventilating air.

Switchgear.—Switchgear can be either very simple or quite elaborate, depending upon the conditions and requirements. Open panels with exposed live parts are not recommended and should never be used on voltages above 600. For larger sets, all equipment should be in grounded steel structures and in many cases switch-gear with removable circuit breakers is justified. The size and ratings of the switchgear will depend upon voltage and current, the interrupting capacity required of circuit breakers and the size and number of inter-connected generators or plants. In all cases, switch-gear should conform to American, AIEE and NEMA Standards.

Tipp City, Ohio, municipal plant with two 1755 hp eight-cylinder, four-cycle, turbocharged dual fuel engines.

In this pumping station at Oakland, California, there are four 1200 hp eight-cylinder, four-cycle Diesel engines with angle gear drives.

CHAPTER FIFTEEN

Selection of Engine Sizes

Three conditions must be fulfilled in selecting the proper size and number of engine units for any power application: (1) sufficient horsepower must be provided to satisfy the maximum demand for power, (2) unit sizes selected should provide power at the lowest total cost for both operating expenses and fixed charges, and (3) provision must be made for future growth. While the foregoing conditions are practically self-evident, it is sometimes difficult to obtain an ideal combination, and consequently it becomes necessary to select that combination of units which most nearly meets all conditions.

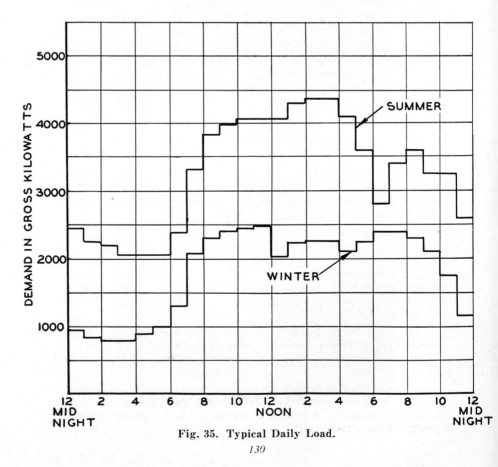

Fig. 35. Typical Daily Load.

Selecting engine sizes for use in central station or industrial power plant service requires careful analysis of the load requirements. This analysis must contain the peak load to be handled at any time; the character of the load, whether continuous or intermittent; the type of the load, giving daily and seasonal variations; the minimum load to be handled, and a forecast of future load requirements.

With the above data at hand, the number and sizes of engines to be installed can be determined. Since there are numerous problems involved, depending on the type of service for which the power is intended, this chapter will present a method for solving an example for a power plant serving a small utility with electricity. A municipal power plant is selected for this example as it includes all of the variations of load encountered in the usual power plant with the exception of industrial power plants operating less than seven days per week.

When specific engine sizes are mentioned in the following discussion it is only for illustrative purposes. The principles are the same regardless of the capacity of the total plant.

Fig. 35 shows the demand for typical summer and winter days of a small municipal electric utility on which the example is based. If a recording watt meter for securing similar data is not available, it will be necessary to read the demand from an indicating watt meter at stated intervals, noting maximum or minimum demands during each interval, and plot the demand from these readings.

For almost every case there will be seasonal variations in the daily demand. It will then be necessary to divide the year into intervals, obtaining a daily demand typical of each interval. Here again the length of the intervals will depend upon the rapidity with which the daily demand shifts. If the change from season to season is gradual, four daily demand curves which are average for each of the four seasons should be sufficient.

Since only a method is being illustrated here, it is assumed that the variation between the winter season and the summer season is gradual and that the two curves on Fig. 35 depict the entire yearly swing in the demand. From Fig. 35, Table 10 is prepared showing the demand for each season and its duration in hours; and a summary table is prepared showing the demand and its duration during the yearly cycle.

From Table 10 a demand duration curve such as Fig. 36 is plotted. This curve illustrates the integrated demand over a period of a year and simplifies the selection of the units for the proposed plant.

For a peak load of 4350 kw the plant firm capacity in engines must also total approximately 4350 kw plus the needs of the near future. Firm capacity is defined as the total plant capacity less the capacity of the largest unit.

Table 10—Seasonal and Annual Integrated Demand

Summer Season		Winter Season		Summary for Year	
Demand Gross kw	Duration hr per yr	Demand Gross kw	Duration hr per yr	Demand Gross kw	Duration hr per yr
4350	365			4350	365
4300	182.5			4300	182.5
4100	182.5			4100	182.5
4050	547.5			4050	547.5
3975	182.5			3975	182.5
3825	182.5			3825	182.5
3600	365			3600	365
3400	182.5			3400	182.5
3300	182.5			3300	182.5
3250	365			3250	365
2800	182.5			2800	182.5
2600	182.5			2600	182.5
		2475	182.5	2475	182.5
2450	182.5			2450	182.5
		2425	182.5	2425	182.5
		2400	547.5	2400	547.5
2375	182.5			2375	182.5
		2300	365	2300	365
2250	182.5	2250	547.5	2250	730
		2225	182.5	2225	182.5
2200	182.5			2200	182.5
		2100	365	2100	365
		2075	182.5	2075	182.5
2050	547.5			2050	547.5
		2025	182.5	2025	182.5
		1750	182.5	1750	182.5
		1300	182.5	1300	182.5
		1150	182.5	1150	182.5
		1000	182.5	1000	182.5
		950	182.5	950	182.5
		900	182.5	900	182.5
		850	182.5	850	182.5
		800	365	800	365

8760 hrs.

Annual Gross Generation = 22,201,125 kwhr

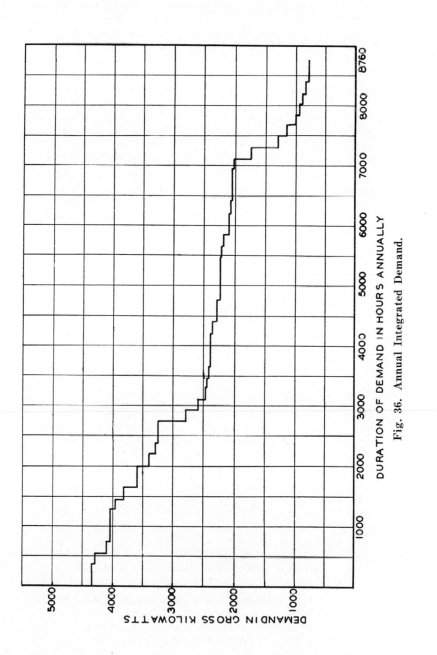

Fig. 36. Annual Integrated Demand.

The selection of unit engine size should not be based only upon existing loads, operating economies and space requirements, but should also reflect anticipated needs for about one decade of growth. The following data should be considered in accurately forecasting growth:

1. Increase in demand recorded in previous years.

2. Geographic location as affecting foreseeable industrial and population growth because of favorable economic factors such as labor, fuel, water, climate, neighboring cities, etc.

3. Attitude of prominent groups and associations which could influence community thinking for or against progress and growth.

4. Growth of neighboring cities or utilities as an indication as to whether past growth (Item 1) accurately reflects expected growth.

5. Immediate prospects of any large increase in load not reflected in past or present records. (New expansion of subdivisions, shopping centers, industrial plants, etc., already planned or in process of construction.)

6. Comparison of load growth forecasts with national averages as a check.

After a careful forecast of system growth has been made, a selection of number of units and unit engine size can be determined by consideration of the following major factors:

1. Reasonable first cost of total plant.

2. Running unit load factor.

3. Fewest number of units practicable.

4. Estimate of cost of plant additions for next decade based on various sized future units.

5. Operating costs estimated over next decade.

6. Financial consideration such as anticipated savings, interest, depreciation and capitalization estimated over next decade.

7. Other specific considerations dictating sizes typical of certain industrial applications.

In addition to the above major considerations, there are others which, if given proper evaluation, can lead to future economies. Unit engine sizes should be large if the forecasts are optimistic. In the years to come this results in fewer unit additions with resultant economies in first cost, floor space, switchgear, material handling facilities, station auxiliaries, etc. In operation, maximum practical unit size means lower labor costs, simpler operation, lower inventory of repair parts and higher unit running time.

Each time expansion of an existing plant becomes necessary, still larger unit sizes should be considered, because the superiority in economy of new units over older can then be felt by their contributing a larger percentage of the generating requirements.

To simplify the example under consideration and to explain the procedure, assume future growth of electric load will dictate a firm capacity of 5000 kw be installed and the number of units held to not more than six. The number of units should be no less than three in order to have reasonable shutdown time for maintenance. Therefore plants of three 2500 kw, four 1667 kw, five 1250 kw, or six 1,000 kw units will be considered. Table 11 shows the average number of hours each unit is in operation each day, and from this table it can readily be seen that each unit can be so operated as to provide enough down time to take care of regular maintenance.

Table 11—Daily Summer Operating Schedule

No. Units in Station	Number of Units Operating—Hours per Day					
	6	5	4	3	2	1
6	0	7	15	24	24	24
5		0	9	17	24	24
4			0	12	24	24
3				0	24	24

The plant-running-capacity factor for each of the above combinations may be obtained from the following equation:

$$\text{Plant-running-capacity factor (PRCF)} = \frac{\text{Gross kw Output}}{\text{Sum of (kw rating ea. unit} \times \text{hrs. ea. unit operated)}}$$

The gross kw output of the plant being considered is 22,201,125 kwhr per year. Table 12 gives the number of hours each group of units operates.

The values in Table 12 are arrived at in the following manner: On Fig. 36 extend a line horizontally from the left ordinate at a point equal to the kilowatt capacity in service to the point where it cuts the demand curve and read the duration of the demand in hours scale at the bottom. Then do the same at the point where this kilowatt capacity is removed from service and the difference between the two durations is the length that this capacity has been in service. For instance, the 3000 kw line cuts the demand curve at 2750 hours and the 2000 kw line cuts the demand curve at 7100 hours. Then the time that the three 1000 kw units have been in service is 7100 hours minus 2750 hours or 4350 hours, which is the amount of time that three 1000 kw units will operate during a year.

Table 12—Yearly Operating Schedule

No. Units in Station	Number of Units Operating—Hours per Year							
	6	5	4	3	2	1	Total	PRCF
6	0	1300	1450	4350	750	910	8760	.800
5		0	1650	1450	4400	1260	8760	.848
4			0	2200	5100	1460	8760	.730
3				0	3100	5660	8760	.752

Table 12 illustrates that the larger the number of units making up the total capacity required, the higher the plant running capacity factor realized. However, Table 11 shows that to obtain this high plant running capacity factor, a greater number of start-ups and shut-downs are necessary. This entails more labor and accelerates engine wear and fatigue.

The comparisons illustrated in Tables 11 and 12 are not conclusive in themselves. It is also necessary to analyze the five (5) basic elements of power cost. These are (1) Fuel, (2) Lubricating Oil, (3) Maintenance—parts and labor, (4) Operating Labor and (5) Amortization, Depreciation and Capital Costs. The following general statements summarize these costs. In an actual example or study, these costs should be calculated for approximately a ten (10) year forecast on the basis of 3, 4, 5 or 6 units.

Fuel Costs.—There would be a small variation in fuel consumption between the 3, 4, 5 and 6 unit plants because of difference in plant running capacity factor. This difference, however, would be quite minor, and would result as much from generator efficiency variation with load as from variation in engine fuel consumption with load. Most modern engines have fuel consumption characteristics such that best economy is realized between 75% and 100% load, and is quite constant within this range. This means that for all intents and purposes, the 3, 4, 5 and 6 unit plants would produce energy for about the same fuel cost.

Lubricating Oil Costs.—Annual lubricating oil costs would be identical for 3, 4, 5 or 6 unit plants. Total lubricating oil consumption is a function of hours operated and is not affected by engine load.

Maintenance—Parts and Labor.—The cost of maintenance for 3, 4, 5 or 6 unit plants will not be the same under most average conditions. Most engine maintenance is concentrated in the combustion area where replaceable parts such as piston rings and fuel injection equipment are located. Labor and parts would be a function of the total number of cylinders in the plant.

It is conceivable, but highly improbable, that the same engine bore and stroke and consequently the same number of cylinders would be used to make up a 5000 kw capacity plant with either 3, 4, 5 or 6 units (2500 kw, 1667 kw, 1250 kw or 1000 kw unit capacity, respectively). Most likely the bore and stroke of small units would be smaller than for larger units and consequently a plant consisting of 6 units of 1000 kw capacity each, as an example, might have twice the total cylinders found in a plant consisting of three 2500 kw units. In this event, renewal parts costs would be slightly less for the plant consisting of fewer large cylinders than for the plant consisting of many small cylinders. Maintenance of smaller parts is less expensive than for large parts, but the difference is not proportional to dimensional size or weight.

Operating Labor.—Operating labor will vary with the number of units in a plant. This labor is required for operation of engines, auxiliaries and switchboard and the keeping of logs tabulating all performance data. It is also required for continuous surveillance of the units to insure safety and reliability of operation. Consequently, the tasks performed by operating crews are somewhat proportional to the number of units they must operate, and it is estimated that one more man per shift would be required to operate 6 units as compared to 3 units.

Amortization, Depreciation and Capital Costs.—The first cost of 3, 4, 5 or 6 unit plants would very likely be quite similar. Here again, it is conceivable but highly unlikely, that the same engine bore and stroke would be used regardless of unit size. If such were the case, of course, then the larger the number of units making up the total capacity required, the higher the first cost. However, generally speaking, a plant of three units would consist of lower speed more expensive units than would a plant of six higher speed smaller units, and because higher speed means lower first cost, the six smaller units themselves would usually be lower in first cost than the three larger units.

In this comparison, other factors than the units themselves must be considered, however, such as building space, number of auxiliaries, switchgear and control equipment and number and size of foundations. These will be less in first cost for a small number of large units than for a larger number of small units.

These two considerations usually equalize each other and the net result is a total plant investment of about the same amount for 3, 4, 5 or 6 units. Amortization and depreciation costs then are also approximately equal.

The life expectancy of a properly maintained heavy duty engine is anywhere from 20 to 30 years.

Summary.—Because of the many variables detailed above, and because forecasting must be done and assumptions made, it is essential that a selection of the number and size of units to be installed be based on studies conducted by individuals and firms with experience and training in this field. A background of utility operation and management is considered essential to forming a correct plan of either initiating a new power plant or expanding an existing plant. Interpretation of all the known facts and the forecastings of the future must be done wisely, and a course somewhere between extreme optimism and pessimism adopted.

CHAPTER SIXTEEN

Power Plant Buildings

Type of Building.—Stationary engines and their associated electrical and mechanical equipment should be provided with adequate housing, either in a new building designed especially for the equipment to be installed, or in suitable space of an existing building which has been remodeled to satisfactorily adapt it to the requirements.

For all except temporary installations and certain industrial installations where first cost is the governing factor, a substantial fireproof building of brick, stone, concrete block or similar construction, with steel framing, should be provided. The services of an experienced architectural engineer, who will incorporate all of the machinery manufacturer's recommendations in the design of the power plant building, is highly recommended unless the buyer has competent engineers to do this work.

Location of Plant.—A modern engine plant has few limitations regarding location, since it produces no smoke; fuel can be stored underground if appearance so dictates; there is no ash disposal problem and no need for unsightly stacks. Proper exhaust and intake air silencing equipment and arrangement eliminate all objectionable noise. The architect can make the external appearance so that it improves the natural beauty of the location in which it is placed.

In selecting the location, consideration should be given to the relative importance of the following:

1. Proximity to the center of power demand.

2. Economical delivery of fuel at the proposed site.

3. Value of property.

4. Suitability of soil for building and machine foundations. Almost any deficiency in this respect can be corrected by special treatment and extra cost, if all factors are known and make it advisable.

5. Possibility for future expansion due to load growth. Consideration must be given to space for increasing fuel storage and cooling, and other auxiliary equipment, as well as building additions to house future main units.

6. Availability of raw water supply for cooling system. It is advisable to choose a location that offers an adequate supply of cooling water at a reasonable pumping or other cost, if this can be done without sacrifice of previously mentioned considerations. However, with the availability of evaporative coolers and modern cooling tower equipment this consideration is not as important as it was some years ago.

Building Design.—In designing the building it is well to decide first on the floor plan arrangement of the main units, laying them out in such a manner as to facilitate installation, maintenance and future additions. Ample space should be provided around each unit to create an attractive overall appearance and provide the greatest ease of maintenance on all engines and auxiliary equipment.

Next consideration should be given to the location of such items and facilities as switchgear, office space, room for tools and operating supplies, shop with bench and facilities for special service work such as injection nozzle maintenance, etc., lockers, toilets and showers for the operating personnel, lubricating oil storage, auxiliary equipment, such as water and oil cooling apparatus, lubricating oil and fuel oil cleaning and purification equipment, etc., always keeping in mind that all auxiliary equipment should be located so as to be adaptable to any future expansion of the plant.

For whatever help they may be to the individual who is designing a specific plant, there are illustrated here two typical plant arrangements. Both of these layouts lend themselves to future expansion with a minimum of expense. One arrangement (Fig. 37) employs a basement for many of the auxiliaries, and also provides an inside location for all air intake filters and exhaust equipment, permitting servicing this equipment without going outside during severe weather such as is encountered in cold northern climates.

The main units in this plant are placed parallel in the engine room which makes unlimited future expansion easy and economical. The switchboard room with desk and engine gage boards is partitioned off from the engine room and is located at the generator end of the main units, permitting the shortest possible electric circuits between the switchgear and generators. Electrically operated oil circuit breakers are used and located in a concrete room or vault in the basement directly under the switchboard panels.

In the basement, on one side of the switchgear vault, is a room containing the auxiliary oil fired heating boiler, and on the other side is the stairway and the lubricating oil storage and purification facilities. Considerable storage space is also provided.

Beside each machine foundation in the basement is located the fuel oil service tank for each respective engine. In many cases an elevated tank is used which is usually mounted on the engine room wall. For insurance purposes, large service tanks are enclosed by concrete walls and covered with sand.

At the end of the basement opposite the switchgear are located all of the lubricating oil coolers, jacket water heat exchangers, oil strainers, jacket water circulating pumps, auxiliary motor driven lubricating oil circulating pumps, and air starting compressors and tanks. The valves for controlling the air starting supply are arranged for operation from the engine room floor level.

For this particular plant, the raw water circulating pumps are located in a separate pump house at the river's edge, which is at

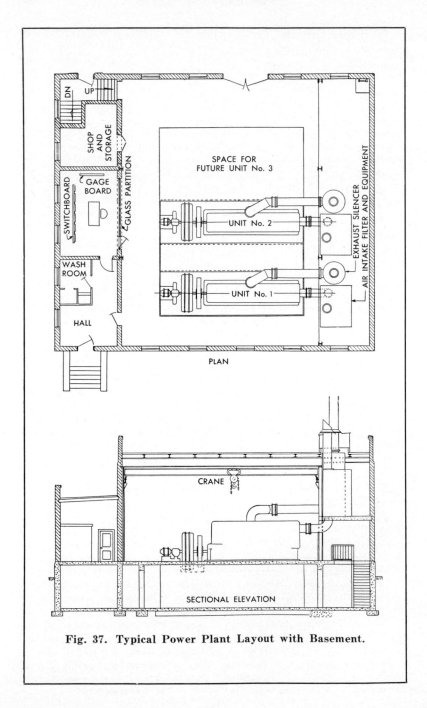

Fig. 37. Typical Power Plant Layout with Basement.

a considerably lower elevation than the basement of the plant. The raw water piping constitutes a closed circuit back to the river, taking advantage of the syphon effect, so that the raw water pumps simply give the water a boost and overcome friction in the circuit. If an abundant supply of raw water were not available, cooling towers could be located adjacent to this end of the building, with the raw water pumps located in the basement similar to the jacket water pump arrangement, or evaporative coolers could be installed where the oil coolers and heat exchangers are now located, making raw water pumps and their piping unnecessary.

This location of the cooling equipment makes the shortest practical piping arrangement to the engines. The basement is designed with ample head room for attractive appearance and ease of movement.

The main stairway from the engine room floor level to the basement is at the end where the cooling equipment is located, and the engine room floor at this point extends only a few feet forward of the engine (sufficient to provide ample passageway) and ends with an attractive railing, leaving an unobstructed view of all cooling equipment in the basement from the engine room floor.

Directly above this open space to the basement, and at an elevation slightly above the engines, is a substantial balcony, supporting the exhaust silencers and concrete air intake filter houses which are provided with heavy hinged steel access doors.

This arrangement permits very short exhaust and air intake piping, effecting a substantial saving in first cost as well as keeping pipe friction at a minimum, which is conducive to the best engine operation. The arrangement also eliminates the hazard, in severe northern locations, of the air filters becoming plugged with snow or ice, causing a forced shutdown of the engines; and further, it permits ease of service of the air filter equipment under any weather conditions and protects the silencers from the weather, as well as eliminates all unsightly stacks and piping on the outside of the building.

For summer operation, this arrangement requires adequate ventilation over the balcony.

The second illustration (Fig. 38) covers a typical plant without a basement.

In this case the external appearance may be improved by using a suitable dividing wall between the engine room and the space occupied by the air intake, exhaust and fuel oil service tank equipment, and by then including all of this equipment inside the outer wall of the building. This arrangement may also be desirable for cold climates.

This illustration shows evaporative coolers mounted on a balcony at the opposite generator end of the engines; however, if heat exchangers and oil coolers are used, necessitating the installation of raw water pumps, it is recommended that space be provided for all of this equipment at the opposite generator end of the engines and located at the engine room floor level, or in a shallow pit.

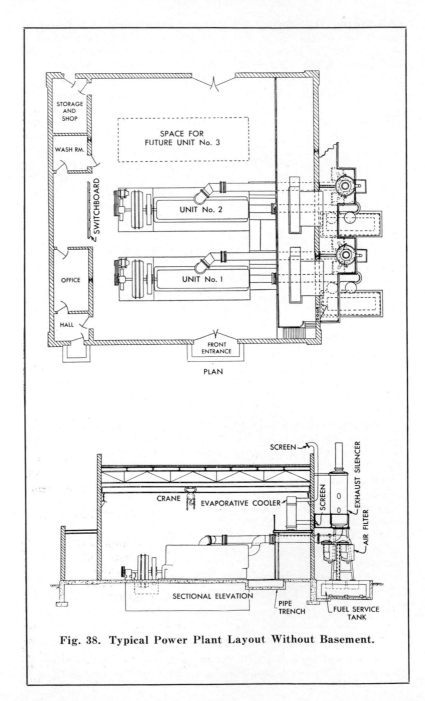

Fig. 38. Typical Power Plant Layout Without Basement.

Building Details.—A comprehensive treatment of building details is beyond the scope of this chapter, and should be handled by a competent and experienced architect who is thoroughly familiar with power plant construction and local conditions. However, the following considerations should be given attention:

1. Provide sufficient head room and suitable overhead crane or other satisfactory method of easily handling all parts requiring periodic service of the machinery now under consideration or likely to be installed at any future time as the load increases.

2. On the side of the building where future units will be installed provide doors which will permit the entrance or exit of any machinery which may be added or removed, and make provision so that any existing unit can be removed, if necessary, without interference with the operation of other units in the plant.

3. If plant is designed without a basement, provide adequate and carefully planned trenches for all piping and electrical circuits.

4. Provide adequate ventilation for all conditions.

5. Provide adequate protective guard railings for flywheel and other moving parts.

6. Provide space for suitable switchboard and control panels, also for maintenance routine and storage of supplies.

7. Hard, non-pourous or glazed surfaces reflect noise while softer, more porous surfaces minimize noise. Therefore porous wall and ceiling surfaces within the building are preferred to reduce the noise level.

Machinery Foundations.—It has become the practice in the industry for engine builders to furnish drawings for engine foundations of appropriate mass and base area, suitable for good footing and also based on the use of good concrete.

Before final details of the foundation design are established, the bearing capacity and suitability of the footings on which the foundations will rest should be determined. In all cases the purchaser should consult an expert in soil mechanics. It may be found advisable to modify the manufacturer's standard drawings to meet special requirements set up by local conditions, by one or a combination of the following:

1. Special reinforcing.

2. Use of a reinforced mat under the regular foundation.

3. Supporting the foundation on piles which may require bracing against horizontal displacement (swaying).

4. Modify the mass as may be required.

Information regarding the values of horizontal and vertical unbalanced inertia forces, and the dead weight of the machinery to be supported, should be obtained from the engine builder. With this information the expert in soil mechanics should assume the responsibility of foundation design to meet the requirements of local conditions.

The installation of foundations is work best handled by local contractors who are better experienced in local soil and other conditions than any engine builder. The foundation work from the first excavation and carpentry to the final grouting covers a much greater range of time than the work of erecting the machinery, and it is not economical to hold the engine builder's erection engineer on the job for this greater period.

The bottom of machine foundations should extend below the footings of the building walls, and the foundations should be isolated completely from the walls and floors of the building.

Foundation blocks should be cast in a single continuous pour, likewise the mat, if used, but the mat and block may be poured separately, in which case they should be tied together by vertical bars.

In installations where there is a possibility of transmission of vibration to adjacent territory, the engine foundations should be insulated by gravel, or mounted on vibration insulating material or devices and installed according to the recommendations of a competent foundation expert.

Turbocharged four-cycle dual fuel 3000 kw generating set in the municipal power plant at Independence, Iowa.

CHAPTER SEVENTEEN

Erection of Engines

Legal Restrictions, Permits and Regulations.—When the purchaser specifies the erection of engines, he should indicate clearly any and all legal restrictions, local ordinances, local special insurance requirements and regulations governing the work to be performed. The buyer must secure any required permits.

Unloading and Hauling.—Specifications covering the unloading and hauling of engines should give (1) the distance from the railroad siding to the place of installation, (2) the type and condition of the streets and roads, or other terrain to be traversed, (3) the type, condition and maximum permissible loading of any bridges and (4) the widths and headroom available at any doors or underpasses.

Buyers, especially municipalities, often have much gear on hand, such as bridge timbers, poles, scaffolding lumber, chain blocks, rope, jacks and tractors, which can be utilized for unloading and hauling purposes. An itemization of such available material in the buyer's specifications will avoid a duplication of facilities on the part of the bidder.

Unloading and hauling should be called for in a separate section of the buyer's specifications in order that specialists on such work and local contractors may submit bids.

Handling of Engine After Delivery.—The engine delivery should be so timed that the building walls, roof and windows, foundations, engine room floors and crane for handling are ready. This will protect the engine from the elements and will reduce the danger of exposing the engine parts to dust and dirt during erection.

If delivery to the plant site is made prior to the time when installation work can proceed without interruption, additional expense and inconvenience, both to the buyer and the engine supplier, are incurred and the machinery endangered. It is recommended that the buyer schedule the completion of building and foundation construction so that the engine can be delivered on its scheduled date and installed without the need for temporary storage and extra handling.

If the building and foundations are not ready for engine erection upon delivery, every precaution should be taken to properly protect the engine and associated parts from the weather and dirt accumulation.

Erection Superintendent.—With the sale of heavy duty engines of the type here discussed, it is strongly recommended that

145

the services of the builder's erecting superintendent be secured for supervising the installation of the engine or engines at a price per diem rate plus travelling and living expenses. Usually such superintendent is available upon reasonable notice from the buyer and remains at the plant until the work is completed and the plant tested or put in operation, or until he is released by the buyer.

Assisting Labor.—Most buyers will find it to their advantage to employ directly all assisting labor for reasons that they are better acquainted with the local labor situation than the engine builder. However, the builder is sometimes requested in the specifications to furnish all erecting labor as well as superintendent. In such case the buyer's specification should give full information as to the rates of pay at which skilled and unskilled labor of the various classes are available in his community.

Erection of Electrical Apparatus.—Engine builders are accustomed to furnish and install generators and exciters driven by their engines, also any motors for driving any auxiliary equipment they furnish. An engine-generator set is of the nature of a complete machine, so that the superintendence of the erection should be unified. Other electrical apparatus and the installation thereof is not related to the engine in that respect, so that it is desirable to segregate such in a separate section to give electrical contractors an opportunity to bid. This section should cover the furnishing and installing of any of the following:

1. Switchgear or sections thereof.
2. Outside electrical structures.
3. All wiring between generators, exciters, switchgear, auxiliaries, outside structures, and for the building, including all cables and conduits.

Auxiliary Foundations, Sumps, Muffler Pits, Trenches.—The installation of all foundations for auxiliaries and all concrete work for sumps, muffler and other pits, trenches and covers, if concrete, should be covered in the section of the specifications covering the building, or the concrete work, if there is a separate section for this.

Plant Piping.—As has been set forth in Chapter Two all engine piping to common inlet and outlet connections is included with each engine.

Engine builders occasionally furnish exhaust and inlet piping in addition to the foregoing. If a buyer wishes this done, he should submit an accurate layout of such piping, showing the exact location of the engine and all auxiliaries, such as the muffler, the air filter, etc., which must be connected.

Buyers of engines are able to buy piping and fittings as advantageously as engine builders. Much of the small piping can scarcely be laid out in advance but should be bought as required. The engine buyer is in the better position to buy and install such piping, under the general supervision of the engine erecting superintendent.

In all cases where the buyer furnishes the plant piping, he should secure the approval of the engine manufacturer as to sizes and arrangement.

It is desirable to paint the piping and/or fittings of the water, fuel, lubricating oil and air starting system with distinguishing colors.

Railings and Guards.—The flywheel generator and exciter of an engine-generator unit should be protected in the interests of safety of personnel. In some states there are laws that govern these matters and these, of course, should be observed. In any event a coaming around the flywheel pit and a pipe railing around the flywheel, generator and exciter are recommended. A sheet-metal guard which encases the flywheel is sometimes a desirable addition to these precautions.

Guards or railings should be made after the unit is installed so that the fits will be accurate. Such work can be best performed by a local sheet-metal shop or pipe fitter, and should be installed when the flooring is poured or laid. Pit coamings, railings and guards should be a part of the floor or building contract. The engine builder should not be requested to furnish or install any such material.

Ten two-cycle 2000 kw Diesel generating sets are installed in the Rincon de Melones Station of the Cuban Electric Company, Havana, Cuba.

CHAPTER EIGHTEEN

Field Test Code

Introduction.—This Test Code is an outline of procedure for commercial testing in the field of low and medium speed stationary Diesel, gas, gas-Diesel, or dual fuel Diesel engine generator units. Mechanical drives and other types of combined units are not included under this code as it is usually impractical to install the necessary apparatus, such as dynamometers, in the field to make the proper measurements and the calculation of the power output from the driven machinery is subject to so many variations that field tests of such drives can only be handled by special agreement between the interested parties.

This test procedure is based on definitions and standards as set forth in Chapter One and in Appendix, page 208. Any other standards may be used by agreement of the parties involved with the understanding that any standards adopted will be used throughout and with proper coordinate values.*

This test code is generally in accord with the ASME Power Test Code No. 17-1949, Reaffirmed 1957, with the exception of certain standards, such as the conditions at which a standard cubic foot of gas is measured.

Object.—The object of a field test is primarily to determine if the engine or engine generator unit included in the contract, when operated under the conditions for which it was sold, meets the performances guaranteed; and secondarily, the collection of data pertaining to the operation of the plant.

The principal determinations are (1) the net power output, and (2) the fuel consumption. If other determinations are required by the contract, test procedure shall be agreed upon by the interested parties.

Power Output Measurement.—The power output of a generator unit shall be measured in kilowatts at the switchboard unless otherwise specified, and the net power output is the kilowatts at the switchboard corrected, if necessary, for certain auxiliaries if used and separately driven. (See Chapter Two, 3rd par.).

Fuel Consumption Measurements.—Because of pipe scale in new lines or foreign matter in newly installed fuel tanks, fuel oil used during a field test may require unusual means for cleaning.

---

* For example: if it is agreed to correct the volumetric reading for gaseous fuel to 68 F, 29.92 inches of mercury and saturated with water vapor, the heating value of the gaseous fuel must also be given in Btu (1hv) per cubic foot of the gaseous fuel at 68 F, 29.92 in. of mercury and saturated with water vapor.

The buyer shall request the engine builder to recommend methods for cleaning and shall supply such equipment.

Liquid fuel consumption shall be determined by direct weighing. Gaseous fuel consumption shall be determined preferably by means of an orifice meter. The orifice meter is preferred because the condition of this type of meter can be easily checked in the field and is therefore more reliable. Construction and installation specifications of orifice meters and factors for determining the flow of gas through orifice meters as given in the A.G.A. Gas Measurement Committee Report No. 3, "Orifice Metering of Natural Gas" (current edition), are to be used in orifice metering of gaseous fuels.

Gaseous fuel consumption may also be determined by means of a positive displacement meter calibrated immediately before and after test.

All gas meter readings shall be corrected to standard conditions of 60 F, 30 inches of mercury at 32 F (14.73 psia) and saturated with water vapor, unless otherwise specifically modified by mutual agreement.*

Time of Test.—The field test should be made promptly after a reasonable run-in period, and under the supervision of the engine builder's engineer.

Preparation for Test.—Before starting the tests, the unit shall be first put in adjustment by the engine builder's engineer. It should then be operated for a sufficient time to assure that it is performing in a normal manner and tests then started immediately.

Test Conditions.—The operating conditions, i.e., the loads, speeds, type of fuel, barometric pressure (or altitude) and ambient temperature during the test shall comply with the contract specifications, and the unit shall be operated in accordance with the engine builder's general recommendations, including lubricating oil type, grade and temperature, cooling water temperature, etc.

Deviation in Operating Conditions.—If the maximum deviation in the operating conditions exceeds permissible values shown in Table 13 the test shall be discarded unless the parties to the test agree otherwise in writing.

Corrections.—Where the deviations in operating conditions are within the limits given in Table 13, the following corrections are to be applied.

    1. Correction of engine rating in accordance with DEMA altitude derating curve. (See Chapter Two, p. 23.)

    2. Correction of engine rating in accordance with the DEMA elevated air temperature derating curve if inlet air temperature exceeds that specified. (See Chapter Two, p. 24.)

---

* See footnote on page 148.

Table 13—Permissible Variations in Engine Tests

Variation of Individual Readings Or Observations From Average		Variation of Average Readings From Specified Conditions	
Load	± 3 %	± 5 %	
Power Factor	± 5 %	± 5 %	
Amperes per Phase	± 5 %	± 5 %	
Rpm	± 1 %	± 2 %	
Barometric Pressure	± 1 %	± 5 %	correction must be applied if below minimum specified.
Intake Air Temperature	± 5 F	± 10 F	correction must be applied if above maximum specified.
Heating Value:			
Liquid Fuel	——	± 3 %	correct for any variation.
Gaseous Fuel	——	± 6 %	correct for any variation.
Hydrogen Content			
Gas Fuel	——	± 4 %	
Gas Pressure at Meter	± 1 %	± 5 %	correct to standard.
Gas Temperature at Meter	± 5 F	± 10 F	correct to standard.
Liquid Fuel Temperature	± 5 F	± 5 F	
Cooling Water:			
Outlet Temperature	± 10 F	± 10 F	
Temp. Rise Thru Engine	± 5 F	± 5 F	

3. Correction of fuel consumption for liquid fuel if heating value of fuel varies from standard 19,350 Btu (hhv) (or that specified) as follows:

$$\begin{bmatrix} \text{Corrected} \\ \text{Fuel} \\ \text{Consumption} \end{bmatrix} = \begin{bmatrix} \text{Fuel} \\ \text{Consumption} \\ \text{as read} \end{bmatrix} \times \begin{bmatrix} \dfrac{\text{Btu (hhv) in fuel}}{19,350 \text{ (or Btu specified)}} \end{bmatrix}$$

4. Correction of fuel consumption in cu. ft. for gaseous fuel engines if low heating value varies from that specified:

$$\begin{bmatrix} \text{Corrected} \\ \text{Fuel} \\ \text{Consumption} \\ \text{in cu. ft.} \end{bmatrix} = \begin{bmatrix} \text{Fuel} \\ \text{Consumption} \\ \text{in cu. ft.} \\ \text{as read} \end{bmatrix} \times \begin{bmatrix} \dfrac{\text{Btu (lhv) in fuel as metered}}{\text{Btu (lhv) specified*}} \end{bmatrix}$$

* See footnote on page 148.

Calibration of Instruments.—Instruments and apparatus used for tests shall be calibrated before and after the test.

Measurements, Observations and Data.—

(a) In order to attain the primary object (see p. 148), the following information must be obtained:

1. Barometric pressure.
2. Intake air temperature.
3. Temperature of gaseous fuel at meter inlet.[1]
4. Pressure of gaseous fuel at meter inlet.[1]
5. Speed in revolutions per minute.
6. Output voltage (per phase).[2]
7. Output amperes (per phase).[2]
8. Power factor.[2]
9. Gross kilowatts output.[2]
10. Gross kilowatt hours output during test period.[2]
11. Kilowatts required to drive certain Engine Assembly items if used and separately driven (see Chapter One, p. 21).[3]
12. Kilowatt hours required to drive certain Engine Assembly items if used and separately driven (see Chapter One, p. 21).[3]
13. Weight or volume of fuel used.
14. Fuel characteristics:

     Liquid Fuel:

    Supplier
    ASTM number
    Gravity API
    Viscosity at 100 F SSU or at 122 F SSF
    Viscosity at 210 F SSU or SSF
    Heating Value, Btu (hhv) per lb.
    Sulfur, percent weight
    BS&W, percent weight
    Carbon residue (Conradson)
    Ash, percent weight
    Flash Point
    Fire Point
    Distillation, percent over at 690 F
    Mid-boiling point for 50% recovered ASTM distillation
    Pour Point
    Cetane number

---

[1] For dual fuel Diesel or gas-Diesel engines.
[2] Measured at the switchboard.
[3] If the power for any Engine Assembly items is obtained from the unit under test and is taken off ahead of switchboard instruments, such auxiliaries are considered as engine driven.

Gaseous Fuel:

Type (Natural, Manufactured, Coke Oven, Sewer, etc.)
Heating value of gas as metered
Temperature of gas as metered
Pressure of gas as metered
Humidity of gas as metered

(b) In order to attain the secondary object (see page 148), the following observations may be made where they are applicable:

1. Pressures:

Scavenging air in manifold
Injection air
Supercharging air in manifold
Gas supply ahead of governor control
Lubricating oil inlet to engine
Lubricating oil inlet to supercharger
Lubricating oil inlet to filter
Lubricating oil outlet from filter
Jacket water inlet to engine
Jacket water outlet from engine
Raw water inlet
Compression of each cylinder
Maximum firing pressure at full load of each cylinder

2. Temperatures:

Engine room
Intake air
Supercharging air in manifold
Exhaust at cylinder outlets
Exhaust at manifold outlet (or turbine inlet)
Lubricating oil inlet to engine
Lubricating oil outlet from engine
Lubricating oil inlet to cooler
Lubricating oil outlet from cooler
Piston cooling fluid from each piston
Jacket water inlet to engine
Jacket water outlet from engine

3. Lubricating Oil Characteristics (for each type used):

Supplier
Trade name
Viscosity at 0 F SSU
Viscosity at 210 F SSU

Instruments and Apparatus.—In order to make the measurements listed under "Measurements, Observations and Data" the following apparatus and instruments are required and are to be furnished by the buyer. Available instruments should be used as far as possible:

(a) Suitable tanks and scales, or meters, arranged for measuring fuel consumed at each load during test.

(b) Pressure gages and manometers to measure the required pressures.

(c) Thermometers and pyrometers to measure the required temperatures.

(d) An engine indicator for taking compression and firing pressures.

(e) A tachometer or frequency indicator.

(f) A revolution counter.

(g) A clock, watch or electrical timing apparatus.

(h) Electrical instruments to measure kilowatts, volts, amperes, power factor and gross kilowatt hour output of the unit, and kilowatt hours required to operate Engine Assembly items (see Chapter One, p. 21), except those mentioned in footnote [3], p. 151.

(i) A water rheostat, unless a steady load of uniform power factor can otherwise be furnished.

(j) Calorimeter for gaseous fuel unless accurate low heating value of the fuel at the engine is available.

(k) Barometer if accurate barometric pressure at site is not available.

Schedule of Preparations.—

(a) Secure proper conditions and functioning of the equipment and check availability of proper loads.

(b) Check and install instruments and apparatus.

(c) Assure uninterrupted jacket water supply.

(d) Assure sufficient fuel supply so that one grade will last throughout the entire test. The fuel shall fulfill the engine contract specifications and shall be furnished by the buyer.

(e) Assure sufficient lubricating oil supply for the test. The lubricating oil shall fulfill the engine contract specifications and shall be furnished by the buyer.

(f) Record general data called for in the test report form as far as available. (See Paragraph below headed "Tabulation of Test Data and Calculation of Results.")

Schedule of Tests.—

(a) The standard tests shall be as follows:
One (1) hour at half load
One (1) hour at three quarters load
Four (4) hours at full load.

(b) Before each test, the engine is brought to steady state under the conditions of the test, the attainment of steady state to be determined by readings which are to be made a part of the record.

(c) During each test period, readings are to be taken and recorded at the beginning and end of test, and at fifteen-minute intervals during test.

(d) A test at 10% overload may be run by special agreement between the interested parties. Such a test is to be run only if the generator manufacturer guarantees his equipment for such overload, and, if run, must be considered approximate only, as generator efficiencies for overload are not guaranteed by the generator manufacturers.

Tabulation of Test Data and Calculation of Results.— The following form is suggested for recording data and results:

(a) General Information:
    Date of test
    Owner
    Location
    Altitude
    Engine builder
    Test conducted by
    Object of test

(b) Description of engine and equipment, including capacities, speeds, makes, types, and other pertinent data.

(c) Test Data and Results:

  1. Data required to attain the engine output as specified. (See (a) in paragraph "Measurements, Observations and Data," p. 151.)

  2. Operating data as specified. (See (b) in paragraph "Measurements, Observations and Data," p. 152.)

  3. Electrical Output:

    (a) Standard generator efficiencies (NEMA).

    (b) Corrected generator efficiency including cable loss to switchboard. (See paragraph "Overall Generator Set Efficiency," p. 157.)

    (c) Deductible kilowatt output required to operate certain auxiliaries if used and separately driven. (See Chapter Two, 3rd Par.), except those mentioned in footnote [3], p. 151.

    (d) Deductible kilowatt hours output required to drive certain auxiliaries if used and separately driven. (See Chapter Two, 3rd Par.), except those mentioned in footnote [3], p. 151.

    (e) Net kilowatt output = gross kilowatt output — deductible kilowatts.

(f) Net kilowatt hours output = gross kilowatt hours
output — deductible kilowatt hours.

4. Net bhp Output:

(a) Net bhp output (mechanical) $= P_m = \dfrac{P_e \times 1.34}{e_g}$

Where P_e = Net kilowatt output
e_g = Corrected generator set efficiency including cable loss.

5. Fuel Quantities:

Oil Fuel:

(a) Net pounds of fuel used per hour =
$W_n = W_a - W_r$

Where W_a = Gross pounds of fuel used per hour
W_r = Recovered uncontaminated
leakage, lb.

(b) Corrected net pounds of fuel used per hour $= W_e$

$W_c = W_n \times \dfrac{F_m}{F_d}$

Where F_m = High heat value of fuel Btu (hhv)
F_d = 19,350 [or Btu (hhv) specified].

Gaseous Fuel:

(a) For tests where the gaseous fuel is metered at
a temperature close to the temperature at standard conditions (60 F) and if extreme accuracy
is not required, no correction for the water
vapor content in the gaseous fuel need be made
and the following applies:

Gaseous fuel consumption in cu ft per hour
as read corrected to standard conditions of
60 F, 14.73 psia*, and assumed to be saturated
with water vapor $= V_a$

$V_a = V_m \times \dfrac{520}{t_m + 460} \times \dfrac{p_m}{14.73}$

Where V_m = Gaseous fuel consumption at
meter as read, cu ft per hour
520 — Absolute temperature at standard
conditions, deg F
t_m = Temperature of gas at meter,
deg F
p_m = Pressure in psia at meter.

---

* See footnote on page 148.

(b) Where extreme accuracy is required or the temperature at which the gas is metered varies widely from standard conditions, as is usually the case with sewage gas, the correction for water vapor in the gas is usually from two to four percent and cannot be disregarded. In such cases, the following formula should be used:

$$V_a = V_m \times \frac{520}{t_m + 460} \times \frac{p_m - p_{mw}}{14.73 - p_w}$$

Where p_{mw} = partial pressure of water vapor in gas at meter, psia

p_w = water vapor pressure at 60 F (0.2563 psia).

(c) Heating value of gaseous fuel at the conditions of temperature, pressure and humidity at which the gas supplied to the engine is metered, in Btu (lhv) per cu ft = F_m.

$$F_m = F_x \times \frac{p_m - p_{mw}}{p_x - p_{xw}}$$

Where F_x = low heating value (lhv) Btu per cu ft of the gaseous fuel at the conditions of temperature, pressure and humidity at which the heating value is determined by the calorimeter

NOTE: The heating value of gaseous fuels as shown by the Junkers type calorimeter is always at 100% humidity unless corrected.

p_x = absolute pressure of the gas at the calorimeter, psia

p_{xw} = absolute partial pressure of water vapor at temperature of gas at calorimeter, psia.

6. Fuel Consumption:

   Oil Fuel:

   (a) Pounds of fuel oil (pilot oil for dual fuel Diesel or gas-Diesel engines) per net kilowatt hour output = w_b

$$w_b = \frac{W_e}{P_e}$$

Where P_e = net kilowatt hours output.

(b) Pounds of fuel oil (pilot oil for dual fuel Diesel or gas-Diesel engines) per net bhp hour $= w_a$

$$w_a = \frac{W_c}{P_m}$$

Where $P_m =$ net bhp output.

(c) Btu (hhv) per net kilowatt hour $= q_d$

$$q_d = w_b \times 19,350 \text{ (or Btu specified)}$$

(d) Btu (hhv) per net bhp hour $= q_c$

$$q_c = w_a \times 19,350 \text{ (or Btu specified)}.$$

Gaseous Fuel:

(a) Btu (lhv) per net kilowatt hour output $= q_b$

$$q_b = \frac{V_a \times F_g}{P_e}$$

Where $F_g =$ Btu (lhv) per cu ft of gaseous fuel at standard conditions of 60 F, 14.73 psia and saturated with water vapor

$P_e =$ net kilowatt output.

(b) Btu (lhv) per net bhp per hour output $= q_a$

$$q_a = \frac{V_a \times F_g}{P_m}$$

Where $P_m =$ net bhp output.

In accordance with Chapter Two, Par. 2, p. 26, the total fuel consumption for gas-Diesel and dual fuel Diesel engines is determined by adding the Btu (hhv) of the pilot oil to the Btu (lhv) of the gas, both as calculated in item 6, p. 156.

Overall Generator Set Efficiency.—

(a) Shaft or brake horsepower output is calculated from the gross kilowatt output after adding the losses occurring between engine and test instruments. Such losses are:

1. I^2R losses of generator stator and rotor coils
2. Core losses
3. Stray load losses
4. Exciter losses (if exciter is driven from the generator shaft)
5. Field rheostat losses, if used
6. Bearing friction and windage losses
7. Friction losses in chains or belts

8. Cable losses (Actual cable losses should be used when available, but in the absence of actual values, it is recommended they be assumed to be 0.3 percent of the rated output of the generator at rated load and to vary as the square of the load.)

9. Brush friction and contact loss in the case of direct current generators.

The procedure in the case of standard designs of engine-driven generators is to subtract from the generator efficiencies a figure to allow for exciter losses, field rheostat losses (if used) and bearing friction and windage[1] losses, if these losses are not included in the efficiencies submitted by the generator manufacturer, and cable losses.

The deductions of Table 14 may be used to account for these additional losses. They are correct within the limits of accuracy of a field test.

Table 14—Overall Generator Set Efficiency Deductions
(Including Assumed Cable Losses in Accordance with item 8)

Full Load Generator Efficiency Not Including Friction and Windage Losses, or Losses in Exciter, Field Rheostat, Chains, Belts and Cable.			Deductions to Obtain Generator Efficiencies Including All Losses[2]		
			Full Load	Three-Quarter Load	Half Load
88.1	to	89	4.0	5.1	8.0
89.1	to	90	3.5	4.6	7.2
90.1	to	91	3.1	4.0	6.3
91.1	to	92	2.6	3.4	5.4
92.1	to	93	2.1	2.8	4.6
93.1	to	94	1.7	2.2	3.7
94.1	to	95	1.2	1.8	2.8
95.1	to	96	0.8	1.1	2.0

If excitation current is furnished from an outside source, these corrections do not apply. For such cases suitable efficiency corrections based upon information secured from the generator builder shall be agreed upon in advance of the test.

When generator efficiencies are guaranteed as overall efficiencies by the generator manufacturer, all the above losses except cable losses are included. These overall efficiencies must be corrected to include the cable losses in accordance with item 8 above in order to determine the net output of the engine.

The power factor shall be maintained at or above that for which efficiencies are specified throughout all tests.

---

[1] When the generator manufacturer supplies the bearings, bearing friction and windage losses are always included in the generator efficiency.

[2] Deduction for each load condition is to be made from the original generator efficiency corresponding to this load condition.

Tests for Governing of Engine Generator Sets.—The object of the following provisions of this Test Code is to outline acceptable methods for measuring the speed changes on engines in order to determine the performance of the governing equipment when desired. Terms used are understood to have the meanings specified in Chapter Four of this book.

1. Apparatus required for Tests of Governing.

To measure departures of speed from a reference speed, it is necessary to employ special instruments which can be either of two types:

(a) A tachograph having a sensitivity of one-quarter of 1%. The instrument shall be calibrated through the range of speed to be measured and a rating curve established for speeds 10% above and 10% below normal speed.

(b) An indicating tachometer of equal sensitivity having a scale which will read from 10% above to 10% below normal speed.

2. Test Methods (governing).

The engine shall be brought to normal speed without load and the behavior of the governor at normal speed without load carefully observed. The speed regulation is measured by gradually applying load to the engine without adjusting the governor, whereas the momentary speed changes are established by suddenly applying or removing loads.

3. Steady-state Operation.

Using tachograph equipment, and with the engine running at normal speed and at any constant load, there should be no erratic movements of the fuel control mechanism. On commercially variable load, the departure from normal speed should be a minimum and the return to steady-state operation should be rapid and positive and without excessive hunting. Unless the load is steady, there will be speed changes introduced due to load fluctuations and the amount of these load fluctuations should not exceed 1% of the full load rating of the engine. If the load changes are greater than this amount it will be necessary to accept the test at no load speed for steady-state operation or provide a water rheostat load free from fluctuations in excess of this amount.

4. Speed Regulation.

To be representative of field operating conditions, the speed regulation shall be measured as follows: With the engine loaded to 100% of rating, adjust the governor to rated speed. No further adjustment shall be made to the governor during the speed regulation determination testing. The load on the engine is then slowly reduced to no load and the speed noted.

5. Momentary Speed Changes and Recovery Time.

In contrast to the determination of the speed regulation with slowly varying loads, the tests for momentary speed changes are made by suddenly applying or removing load from the engine. The momentary overspeed is the difference between the maximum momentary speed and the final steady-state speed following an instantaneous load decrease expressed as a percentage of the steady-state speed at the time of load change. Momentary underspeed is similarly determined. See Chap. Four, page 37. The recovery time is measured as the time from the initial load change until the speed has reached and remains within the prescribed speed band corresponding to the new steady-state load. See Chap. Four, page 37, and Fig. 3, page 37. The speed will not return to the previous speed but will remain above or below it by the amount of speed regulation corresponding to the amount of load change except for isochronous governing on units running alone.

With electrical generating units, it may be possible to open the circuit breaker or oil switch and remove load instantaneously from the engine. Under these conditions, the measurement of the momentary speed change can be observed on the indicating tachometer or by the record on the chart of the tachograph. The momentary speed change can be measured either above or below the speed at the instant of sudden variation of load, depending upon whether the load is applied or removed. Both types of load changes should be tested if possible, but in the event the load cannot be suddenly applied, the test for maximum momentary speed change will be established by the reduction or tripping of load from the engine.

M and A Electric Power Cooperative's Green Forest Generating Plant in Poplar Bluff, Missouri, operates four four-cycle turbocharged dual fuel 2350 kw generating sets.

CHAPTER NINETEEN

Suggestions Covering the Preparation of Invitations For Bids and Detailed Specifications

General.—Invitations for formal, sealed bids should state the date and hour of the opening of bids, set forth a list of the machinery to be furnished and the work to be done, state the terms offered for payment and, if the buyer is a municipality, cite the legal authorization for the purchase and the source of the funds from which payments will be made.

This chapter deals mainly with larger sizes of engines for which detailed specifications for the engine proper, its accessories and its auxiliaries can be defined and custom tailored to the requirements of specific applications and installation conditions. This is possible only to a limited degree with smaller engines because of the nature of their design and standardization. Some of the most frequently encountered practices for small sizes of engines which vary from their larger counterparts, are as follows:

1. Ratings are based on (a) maximum output, (b) intermittent output and (c) continuous output, and these are stated for sea level, 60 F ambient conditions and may be with or without engine driven accessories. The continuous rating may be as much as 30% below the maximum rating.

2. Standards of speed and voltage regulation are not stated for smaller size of engines. Mechanical governors and manufacturers standard voltage regulator are usually furnished.

3. No fuel or lubricating oil consumption guarantees are made. Only estimates are given.

4. Smaller size engines usually include switchgear and cooling system.

5. Installation, unloading and hauling are not furnished with smaller engines.

6. No specific fuel systems are furnished. An engine driven fuel pump, filter and engine mounted fuel tank are available.

7. No recommendations for foundation are made but common subbase is usually furnished.

8. No piping external to engine is furnished.

9. Lubricating oil cooler (if required) is usually built into crankcase and is in the jacket water circuit.

10. Starting is either by hand crank or 12 volt electric starting system. The latter is extra and may include generator, voltage regulator, starting motor and battery with leads and trickle charger.

11. Gauge board is engine mounted and includes only lube oil pressure gauge, water temperature gauge and battery ammeter.

12. Safety controls include only overspeed shutdown. An alarm system can be furnished as an extra for low lube oil pressure and/or high jacket water temperature and automatic shutdown for these reasons can be furnished, also as an extra.

13. It is possible to specify only the function of engine accessories and not their type of make.

14. Intake filters are usually furnished with engine.

15. Crankcase breather filters are usually furnished.

16. Lubricating oil filter is furnished.

17. Design details of engine proper cannot be modified due to rigid standardization of the product.

The following suggestions covering the preparation of invitations for bids and detailed specifications apply chiefly to engines of 500 hp and larger, and should be modified for smaller engines in line with the above.

Detailed specifications should state the location and altitude of the proposed installation, the number and approximate sizes of the engines to be furnished, the nature of the driven machinery, auxiliaries and appurtenances the engine builder does not make but is expected to furnish, the details of the equipment to be furnished and the work to be done by contractors other than the engine builder, and the amount of equipment to be furnished and the work to be done by the buyer.

The suggested forms for invitations and specifications presented in this chapter have been prepared with these precepts in mind. Since sealed bidding is the general rule in municipal or other governmental transactions, the forms are applicable in detail to that type of purchase, although slight modifications will adapt the text to the needs of the private buyer.

Specifications and contract documents for a municipal or other governmental project must conform strictly with applicable laws in order to avoid litigation initiated by interests adverse to the project. For this reason, as well as the fact that the engine builders are accustomed and prepared to handle mainly the engine generator unit with its related accessories and auxiliaries as specified in Section 1, it is suggested that specifications be divided into sections with each contractor free to bid upon any or all sections. By this division, the work of each contractor will be exactly defined and his contract will not be invalidated by any changes made in other work. Also, the work will be done more economically by eliminating unnecessary subcontracting.

All engine builders have standard contract forms which are drafted to protect both buyer and bidder. If such forms are not recognized, many bidders feel obliged to take exception to the form of agreement proposed by the buyer. Often a bid with such exceptions is otherwise so acceptable that the bidder is awarded the contract even though the award may be open to attack because of such exceptions. The *Notice to Bidders* and the *Proposal* which follow make provisions for utilizing the bidder's contract form.

The indiscriminate distribution of plans and specifications to all firms or individuals who might request them without serious intentions of submitting bids, results in unnecessary expense. The requiring of a nominal deposit on each set of plans and specifications is justified, which deposit should of course be refunded in full upon the return of each set. This is now customary among the more prominent consulting engineers.

Invitation for Bids.—A suggested form of invitation to bidders is presented herewith:

NOTICE TO BIDDERS

Sealed bids will be received by_____until
(name and address of Buyer)

_____ o'clock, standard time, the _____day of_____, 19_____,
at_____and publicly opened, for the furnishing
(designation of office)
of machinery, materials and services as follows:

Section 1

___( ) (Diesel) (Dual Fuel) (Gas) Engine(s) of the manufacturer's standard rating of not less than _____ bhp (each) at a speed of not to exceed _____ rpm.

___( ) (Diesel) (Dual Fuel) (Gas) engine(s) of _____ etc.

___( ) (Diesel) (Dual Fuel) (Gas) engine(s) of _____ etc.

Electric generator(s) and exciter(s) of size(s) required for the engine(s) offered.

Miscellaneous engine equipment and accessories.

The above shall be furnished f.o.b. manufacturer's plant, with freight allowed to destination as specified.

Erection superintendent shall be furnished at the_____
(Bidder's) (Buyer's)
expense. All other labor shall be furnished at the buyer's expense.

Section 2

Switchgear.

All cables and conduits.

Other electrical apparatus, namely_____etc.

The above shall be furnished f.o.b. manufacturer's plant, with freight allowed to destination as specified.

Section 3

External cooling system, delivered and erected.

Section 4

Fuel oil storage system, delivered and erected.

Section 5

Gaseous fuel system, delivered and erected.

Section 6

Unloading and hauling of all mechanical and electrical equipment of Sections No. 1 and 2, from cars at_____ and hauling of such equipment to the site at_____ removing skids and placing on foundations.

Section 7

Power plant building, machinery and equipment foundations, and all concrete work.

All equipment, material and services shall conform to plans and specifications on file in the office of_____ in the City of_____. All bids shall be accompanied by a bidder's bond (certified check on a solvent bank) in the amount of_____percent* of the bid price. Bidder's bonds of unsuccessful bidders will be returned to them immediately upon award of contracts. (Certified checks of unsuccessful bidders will be returned upon award of contracts but in any event not later than 30 days from date of receipt of bids). _____

(Name of Buyer)

proposes to pay contractors for the sections covered by the specifications, as follows:

(itemize schedule of payments)

_____

_____

_____

_____

Note: Payments are usually made to parallel the approximate progress of the work. In the case of large contracts, progress payments are often made periodically upon certification by the engine builder of progress made at his plant. Such progress may be reported monthly or quarterly. If progress payments are not made, then it is customary to make an initial payment of approximately 25% with the order and a substantial payment of 50% to 65% on shipment of the engine. The final payment of usually about 10% is made upon completion of the work and acceptance by the buyer.

_____

_____

---

* Usually about 5%.

The funds for this purpose are legally available to ....
(name of Buyer)
.... through (insert circumstances of any bond issue,
popular referendum, etc.) ....
....
....

Bids will be received separately on each section of the specifications. Each bidder will submit with his proposal a form of agreement
in general conformity with the requirements set forth in the notice
to bidders. A successful bidder shall, within ...... days (legal period)
after the receipt of notice of the award to him, execute with................
........................the agreement in the form submitted as aforesaid.
(name of Buyer)
Minor changes in such agreement form approved by........................
(name of Buyer)
and Bidder after the award of the contract shall not invalidate said
award. Should the successful bidder fail to execute, within said
period, the form of agreement satisfactory to both Buyer and Bidder, Buyer shall be entitled to cancel his acceptance of the bid and
award the contract to another bidder if in Buyer's judgment it is
considered desirable to do so. ....reserves the
(name of Buyer)
right to reject any and all bids. Dated this ...... day of ....,
19......

City Clerk	*Mayor*

Form for Bidders.—A suggested proposal form for bidders is
presented herewith:

PROPOSAL

The ...., hereinafter called "Bidder," hereby
(name of Bidder)
proposes to furnish ...., hereinafter called "Buyer,"
(name of Buyer)
machinery and auxiliaries, freight allowed to siding at........................,
and services at the site, as called for in the attached specifications,
and in accordance with the provisions of the same at the following
prices:

Section 1

........( ) engine-generator set(s), together with all equipment
and services specified in the respective items of Section 1 of the
attached specifications:
Price: Section No. 1........................($........)

Section 2

Switchgear, ...($........)
(Sections 2, 3, 4, 5, 6, and 7 to be handled in the same
way as Section 1).

Bidder reserves the right to refuse an award of contract which does not include all of the following:

(Bidder lists here the minimum combination of sections and items thereof for which he will enter into contract.)

Bidder agrees to enter into contract, and to furnish a performance bond in the penal sum of _____ percent of the contract price, within _____ days (legal period) from the date of Buyer's acceptance of this proposal and to ship all material specified in this proposal within _____ weeks from the date the contract is signed by Buyer and accepted by Bidder, and Buyer has notified the Bidder that any and all legal or financial details have been satisfied to insure a firm and binding contract upon both parties.

If this proposal is signed by Bidder and accepted by Buyer, and should Bidder, for any reason, fail to execute the contract within _____ days (legal period) after the award of the same, or fail to furnish performance bond, and/or other bonds required by law, the bid bond (certified check), which has this day been deposited with Buyer, shall, at the option of the latter, be forfeited to him as liquidated damages, but otherwise the bid bond (certified check) shall be returned to Bidder when the executed contracts are delivered to Buyer.

Bidder attaches his standard contract form in duplicate to this proposal. Such contract form shall apply to this transaction if Buyer awards this contract to Bidder. In the event of such award, Buyer will execute such standard contract form in duplicate and return to Bidder, who shall execute one copy and return it to Buyer.

Dated at_____, this _____ day of _____, 19_____

| (name of Bidder) | (address of Bidder) |

By _____
Title _____

Warranty or Guarantee of Workmanship and Materials.

—It is recommended that wherever practical the Standard Warranty of the engine manufacturer be used. In cases where such a warranty is not available, the following form is offered as a suggestion: The Bidder guarantees that the machinery manufactured by it which it proposes to furnish hereunder will be well made, of good material and in a workmanlike manner, and that if, within one year from the date of starting the engine after delivery but not exceeding 18 months from date of shipment, any guaranteed part should fail because of defective material or workmanship in the manufacture thereof and specific written notice of such failure be given the Bidder within such time, the Bidder shall replace such defective part, free of charge, f.o.b. cars its factory; provided, that, at the option of the Bidder, parts claimed to be defective shall be returned to the Bidder's factory for inspection, with all transportation charges thereon prepaid by the Buyer.

All guaranties and warranties with respect to machinery, apparatus accessories, materials, or supplies not manufactured by the Bidder shall be limited to the respective guaranties or warranties of the manufacturers thereof. The Bidder shall not be liable for any repairs or alterations except those made with its specific written consent and approval and shall not be liable for damages or delays, whether caused by defective material or workmanship or otherwise; and it is expressly agreed that all liability of the Bidder with respect to said machinery, or its use or operation, including that under any and all guaranties, or warranties, whether express or implied, is strictly limited to the replacement, in the manner aforesaid, of guaranteed parts failing, within the time hereinbefore stated, by reason of defective material or workmanship in the manufacture thereof.

Detailed Specifications.—The following detailed specifications are not intended for rigid application to each and every project. They are typical only, and equipment specified may be changed to meet the buyer's needs. For example, shell and tube type heat exchangers may be used instead of the atmospheric type shown in the following sample specifications, or an evaporative cooler or radiator may be employed instead of the cooling tower with heat exchangers.

Other similar changes may also be desirable. Local conditions will often point the way to modifications. Such conditions may include not only the kind of plant to be built but also the class of contractor operating locally. In some districts, the contractors may be organized to take work which cuts across the Sections here suggested. The buyer should take such local situations into account.

Certain specifications are so well standardized that it is unnecessary for any elaboration to be made herein. Such are specifications for building in general, and masonry, brickwork, steel framing, sash, doors, outside electrical structures, etc., in particular. Specifications for such items will be presented in outline only.

SPECIFICATIONS
Power Plant for the

(name of Buyer)

General

The machinery, auxiliary equipment, building(s), work and services covered by these specifications are to furnish_____
(name of Buyer)
with a (electric power plant) (electric generating unit) to be located at _____
The prices specified in the bidder's proposal shall include the sup-

plying of materials and the performance of work as described in the respective Items and Sections.

Definitions

The following terms, whenever occurring in these specifications, are to be understood to have the meanings here set forth:

"Buyer" means _____
(name and address of Buyer)

"Engineer" means _____
(name and address of engineer)

who (has been retained) (is employed) by Buyer to plan and supervise the construction of the plant covered by these specifications.

"Site" means _____, which is the future location of the plant covered by these specifications.

"Siding" means the siding at _____, the standard gage railroad siding nearest the site, connecting with the _____ Railroad.

"Bidder" means the Bidder on the section in which the term is used.

"Others" means the Buyer and/or one or more of the bidders on sections other than the one in which the term is used.

"Builder" means the builder of the equipment referred to, whether or not a bidder in his own name.

"Specifications" means these specifications.

"Plans" means the drawings prepared by the Engineer, these forming part of these specifications. Such drawings are numbered as follows:

Drawing No. _____

Drawing No. _____

Drawing No. _____

etc.

"A.G.A." means American Gas Association, 420 Lexington Ave., New York 17, N. Y.

"AIEE" means American Institute of Electrical Engineers, 29 W. 39th St., New York 18, N. Y.*

"API" means American Petroleum Institute, 50 W. 50th St., New York 20, N. Y.

"ASA" means American Standards Association, 70 E. 45th St., New York 17, N. Y.

"ASME" means American Society of Mechanical Engineers, 29 W. 39th St., New York 18, N. Y.*

"ASTM" means American Society for Testing Materials, 1916 Race St., Philadelphia 3, Pa.

"DEMA" means the Diesel Engine Manufacturers Association, 2000 K St., N.W., Washington 6, D. C.

"DEMA Standard Practices" means the Standards outlined in the "Standard Practices for Low and Medium Speed Stationary

---

* In 1960 the address will be United Nations Plaza (formerly First Ave.) at 47th St., New York 17, N. Y.

Diesel and Gas Engines" of the Diesel Engine Manufacturers Association (1958).

"NBFU" means the National Board of Fire Underwriters, 85 John St., New York 38, N. Y.

"NEMA" means the National Electrical Manufacturers Association, 155 E. 44th St., New York 17, N. Y.

"SAE" means the Society of Automotive Engineers, 485 Lexington Ave., New York 17, N. Y.

"C" means degrees Centigrade.

"F" means degrees Fahrenheit.

"hhv" means high heat value.

"lhv" means low heat value—saturated with water vapor when applied to gas.

"psi" means pounds per sq. inch.

"SSF" means Saybolt Seconds Furol.

"SSU" means Saybolt Seconds Universal.

Information for Bidders

Buyer sets forth the following information which has bearing on this project for an Electric Power Plant:

1. Buyer's form of government _____
2. Government incorporated _____ 19____
3. Classification of Municipality _____
4. Town, City, and/or County Seat _____
5. Population, last census _____
6. Assessed valuation of city property, year 19____ $_____
7. Tax rate _____
8. Income from taxation and assessments, year 19____ $_____
   Less total expense, city depts. $_____
   Less interest, general obligation bonds $_____
   Less retirement on such bonds $_____ $_____
   Balance $_____

   (If a power plant is now in operation, list the annual gross revenue for a period of three years, and show deductions for operating expense, capital expenditures, interest and retirement on bonds.)

9. Bonded indebtedness; all outstanding bonds:

Amount Yearly	Date of issue	Date of maturity	Interest rate	Purpose	Yearly retirement	Sinking fund
----	----	----	----	----	----	----
----	----	----	----	----	----	----
----	----	----	----	----	----	----
----	----	----	----	----	----	----
----	----	----	----	----	----	----
----	----	----	----	----	----	----

   (If a power plant is now in operation, list separately bond data applicable to it.)

10. All matured bond issues of the municipality have been paid to date, (except _____).

11. Other obligations of Buyer, or any of its departments, not listed in the foregoing are _____

12. Cash on hand is as follows:
    Electric light and power fund $_____
    Water fund $_____
    General fund $_____
    Other funds $_____

    A copy of the latest financial report, audited by a firm of certified public accountants, is attached hereto (including the audit of the Electric Light and Power Department).

13. Buyer and the city residents are now being served by (a municipally owned plant) _____
    (name of private power company)
    (If served by a municipally owned plant, state when established, present generating capacity installed in kilowatts, number and size and type of prime movers installed, output in kilowatt-hours by years for the past three years, present replacement value of plant and depreciated value.)

*14. The annual consumption in kilowatt-hours by the city and residents in the year 19____ was as follows:

	No. of services	Total kwhr	Total dollars paid
Domestic Light and Appliances	----------	----------	----------
Special Domestic, namely ----,	----------	----------	----------
----,	----------	----------	----------
----,	----------	----------	----------
Small Light and Power	----------	----------	----------
Large Light and Power	----------	----------	----------
Industrial	----------	----------	----------
Water Department	----------	----------	----------
Street Lighting	----------	----------	----------
City Buildings	----------	----------	----------
Other City uses, namely ----,	----------	----------	----------
----,	----------	----------	----------
----,	----------	----------	----------

*15. The total connected motor load of the system, including all types of services, is _____ horsepower.

*16. Buyer (plans to sell) (sells) (will not sell) electric light and power to customers outside the city limits.
    (If now selling in such areas, specify to whom, with what yearly revenue, whether or not on contracts, when contracts expire, rates charged, demand in kilowatts, etc.)

----

* Data requested in items 14 to 19 inclusive not required except when the municipality is initially entering the public power generation field.

*17. Buyer (owns) (does not own) the distribution system which will be used. (The present replacement value of such system is \$_____, the depreciated value is \$_____).

*18. Manufacturing industries within the city limits are as follows:
Number of factories _____.
Principal products _____
_____
Markets _____
_____

(*state geographical districts in which the products are sold*)

Approximate Number of Employees _____

*19. Rates charged for electric service are now as follows:
Domestic rate, general _____
                special, namely for _____
                special, namely for _____
Small Light and Power _____
Large Light and Power _____
Industrial _____
Water Department _____
Street Lighting _____
City Buildings _____
Other City uses, namely for _____
_____
_____

20. (No) Litigation is threatened or proposed in regard to this purchase. (Such litigation may be along the following lines: _____)

21. Members of the Buyer's governing body are:
_____   _____
                                                  (*Mayor or Chairman*)
_____   _____

22. Buyer proposes to provide funds for this purchase by _____

(*Describe any bond issues and state whether or not underwritten, and if so, by whom*)

23. The altitude of the site is _____ ft above sea level.

Equipment to be Furnished and Work to Be Performed by the Buyer

Buyer hereby agrees to furnish the following equipment and perform the following services in connection with the construction of the power plant covered by these specifications:

1. Obtain all permits for the transportation, installation and operation of any machinery, equipment, and constructions requiring permits.

2. Furnish the successful bidder with copies of any State and local regulations governing the installation of machinery, equipment, or construction.

---

* See footnote page 170.

3. Acquire the real estate for the site in fee simple and unencumbered, except for general obligations noted in the foregoing.

4. Perform all grading, including cuts and fills, necessary to bring the site to grade, and establish basic reference lines and levels.

5. Construct all roadways (and siding) required on the site.

6. Construct any retaining walls, curbs, fences, gates, sidewalks on the grounds of the site.

7. Perform landscaping on the grounds of the site.

8. Furnish water and sewer connections of the size required for construction purposes and for operation of the plant, such connections to be within the limits of the grounds of the site.

9. Permit free access to, and storage of materials on, the site, such permission to be granted to the successful bidders.

10. Furnish water, and the use of the following equipment, free of charge, to the successful bidders, in the order of priority of request:

(List all equipment available, such as bridge timbers, poles, scaffolding lumber, chain blocks, rope, jacks, tractors, etc.; often much equipment of this nature can be borrowed by the Buyer from the railroad delivering the machinery.)

11. Furnish protection against weather and theft for all contractor's materials and equipment stored at the site.

12. Assume responsibility for protection and storage of engine and equipment during period after delivery and before start of erection, if erection of engine is delayed by buyer. In the event that this delay necessitates extra handling and/or reconditioning, buyer will assume the costs thereof.

13. Any other items to be furnished by the Buyer should be listed, such as labor for installation, labor and equipment for unloading and hauling, station piping, switchgear and wiring, foundations, building or building changes, crane (which shall be available during erection of engine and equipment), cooling tower, fuel storage tanks, starting air equipment, etc.

Section 1

Engine-Generator Set(s), Equipment and Services

Item 1:

The Engine(s) covered by this Item shall be two- or four-cycle; vertical (horizontal); trunk piston, crosshead, opposed piston, single or double acting; air or mechanical injection; Diesel; dual fuel; gas; and shall be of the standard design of the bidder. (The) (Each) engine shall be furnished with at least the minimum equipment according to DEMA Standard Practices. The bhp rating(s), required auxiliaries, the guarantees of fuel consumption, acceptance tests, parallel operation, governor performance, torsional vibration, and materials and workmanship shall be in accordance with DEMA

Standard Practices. (The) (Each) engine shall be equipped with a (centrifugally-powered) (relay-powered) governor, with (hand-) (remote, switchboard-) control apparatus. (The) (Each) engine shall be furnished with the bidder's standard platform and ladder. (The engines shall be furnished with connecting platforms as shown on the plans, which give exact locations for all engines, connecting runways and ladders [stairs]).

The size(s), speed(s), and other characteristics of the engine(s) furnished shall be as follows:

Item No. 1 (a) : Not less than _____ bhp nor more than
_____ bhp. Not to exceed _____ rpm.

Item No. 1 (b) : Not less than _____ bhp nor more than
_____ bhp. Not to exceed _____ rpm.

Item No. 1 (c) : Not less than _____ bhp nor more than
_____ bhp. Not to exceed _____ rpm.

For installations at altitudes above 1500 feet, both sea level and specified altitude ratings shall be furnished.

The engine(s) and equipment of Item No. 1 are to be furnished f.o.b. the builder's works, with freight allowed to siding.

(The) (Each) engine is to be furnished with an extension shaft, including coupling, coupling bolts, and generator (and exciter) key(s), and outboard bearing suitable for mounting an engine-type generator and (direct-connected exciter) (pulley for belted exciter, including driving pulley, belt and guard).

Erection superintendent shall be furnished at the expense of _____
_____. If at the expense of the bidder, such services
     (Buyer)   *(Bidder)*
shall consist of _____
_____

The successful bidder shall submit certified setting plans for (the) (each) engine-generator set, _____ days after the signing of the contract. Excavation, and design and construction of foundations will be performed by others.

Each bidder shall furnish data applying to the engine(s) offered on the equipment data form attached to these specifications.

Item 2:

The Electric Generator(s) covered by this Item (is) (are) of the _____ type. (It) (Each) shall be for three phase, 60-cycle, _____ volt, alternating current. Generator(s) shall be of recognized, standard make, designed and constructed in accordance with the latest American Standards and NEMA Standards.

The generator(s) (is) (are each) to have a kilowatt rating, at _____ percent power factor, which will absorb the full rating of the (corresponding) engine(s) of Item No. 1. The generator speed(s) shall correspond to the speed(s) of the (corresponding) engine(s) of Item No. 1. The generator(s) shall be of open type, capable of carrying full rated load continuously under standard conditions without exceeding temperature ratings in accordance with NEMA standards depending on class of insulation.

Each generator pole piece shall be provided with damper windings. Slide rails or sole plates, providing for stator shift, shall be provided (with each generator) if required. Field windings shall be for 125 volts, direct current.[1]

The generator unit(s) covered by these specifications will be required to operate in parallel with the following units now installed:

(List complete nameplate data, also type, capacity and speed of prime mover for each unit.)

(The) (Each) generator is to be furnished with a (direct connected) (belt or chain driven) exciter of sufficient capacity to provide the required excitation for the generator, the exciter rating to be on a basis of 125-volts and 40 C temperature rise. Windings of (the) (each) exciter shall be (shunt) (compound). The rated speed of the (direct connected exciter is to be the same as that of the [corresponding] generator) (belted or chain driven exciter shall not exceed _____ rpm). (Direct connected exciter[s] are to be furnished with necessary sole plates or mounting[s]). (Belted or chain driven exciter[s] [is] [are] to be furnished with pulley[s] and base[s]). Generator efficiencies are to be determined by the latest methods recommended by American Standards. The generator(s) (is) (are) to be given the usual factory commercial tests.

(The) (Each) generator shall be furnished with (manual-type) (automatic) generator and exciter field rheostats and field discharge resistors for (back-of-board) (other) location, including operating gear. Generator(s) and exciter(s) are to be furnished f.o.b. the builder's works, with freight allowed to the siding. Each bidder shall furnish data applying to the generator(s) and exciter(s) offered on the equipment data form attached to these specifications.

Item 3.

Auxiliaries:

(a) Pyrometer Equipment.—The successful bidder shall furnish complete pyrometer equipment of _____ make, or equal, for (the) (each) engine specified in Item No. 1, including: thermo-couples installed in place in (the) (each) engine; all leads, cables and conduits from said thermo-couples to the indicating instrument(s); and _____ indicating instrument(s) (The) (Each) indicating instrument shall have at least _____ switch points, and shall be for mounting on the (switchboard) (wall) (engine).[2] Each bidder shall furnish data applying to the

---

[1] Excitation voltage may be 250 for large capacity generators.
[2] Pyrometer equipment in plants already existing can often be modified by changing the instrument switch to take care of additional units. It is advisable to communicate with the maker of the pyrometer for his suggestions.

pyrometer equipment offered on the equipment data form attached to these specifications.

(b) Exhaust Muffler(s).—The successful bidder shall furnish an exhaust muffler for (the) (each) engine of Item No. 1. Such muffler(s) shall be of the engine builder's or other standard make, of cast iron or welded steel, and shall be equipped with companion flanges. (The) (Each) muffler shall be for installation in accordance with detailed plans. (If there are any special requirements for exhaust muffling, these should be detailed here.) Each bidder shall furnish data applying to the exhaust muffler(s) offered on the equipment form attached to these specifications.

(c) Intake-Air Muffler(s).[1]—The successful bidder shall furnish an intake-air muffler for (the) (each) engine of Item No. 1. Such muffler(s) shall be of the engine builder's or other standard make, of cast iron or _____ steel, and shall be equipped with companion flanges (and air-intake bonnet[s][2]). (The) (Each) muffler shall be for installation in accordance with detailed plans. Each bidder shall furnish the data applying to the intake-air muffler(s) offered on the equipment data form attached to these specifications.

(d) Air Filter(s).—The successful bidder shall furnish an air filter for the intake air for (the) (each) engine of Item No. 1, these to be of _____ make, or equal. (This) (These) shall be of the (dry) (wet) type. (The) (Each) filter shall be furnished with companion flanges, weather louvres and accessories if required. The filter(s) shall be for installation in accordance with detailed plans. Each bidder shall furnish data applying to the filter(s) offered on the equipment data form attached to these specifications.

(e) Starting Air Plant.[3]—The successful bidder shall furnish a starting air plant, including a (Diesel engine-) (gasoline engine-) (motor-) driven air compressor, and air storage tank or tanks. The air compressor shall be (single-) (two-) (three-) stage,[4] (hopper) (jacket) (air) cooled, and shall be suitable for a discharge pressure equal to the starting air pressure recommended by the engine builder for the engine(s) of Item No. 1. The compressor may be (mounted on a common base) (furnished) with the (Diesel engine) (gasoline engine) (electric motor),[5] which shall also be furnished, the (engine) (motor) to be (direct connected) (geared) (connected by short belt drive) to the compressor. (The engine shall be complete

[1] This equipment may not be required.
[2] Air-intake bonnets are not required if air filters are to be used.
[3] When buying new generating units for an existing plant, specifications should state the number, capacity and working pressure of the existing air tanks, also the size of the starting compressor installed.
[4] Single-stage is satisfactory for 200 psi and under, for smaller capacity.
[5] A single compressor may be arranged for dual drive from either engine or electric motor.

with fuel tank and ready to run.) (The electric motor shall be furnished with starting switch and shall be arranged for three phase, 60-cycle, 220-volt current.)* The air tank or tanks shall have a total capacity equal to that recommended by the builder of the engine(s) of Item No. 1 for the (number and) size of engine(s) covered by Item No. 1. The tank or tanks shall be designed and built in conformity with the latest ASME Standards for the recommended starting air pressure (and shall also conform to the regulations of the State of _____, and of _____, which regulations are attached hereto). (The) (Each) tank shall be cylindrical and shall be furnished with a main valve, drain valve, relief valve, pressure gage and supporting feet. Each bidder shall furnish data applying to the starting air plant offered on the equipment data form attached to these specifications.

(f) Lubricating Oil Cooler(s).—The successful bidder shall furnish a lubricating oil cooler for (the) (each) engine of Item No. 1. Water (specify source and conditions) is available at _____ F. The lubricating oil cooler is to be furnished f.o.b. the builder's works, with freight allowed to the siding. Each bidder shall furnish data applying to the cooler furnished on the equipment data form attached to these specifications.

(g) Lubricating Oil Centrifuge(s) or Purifier(s).—The successful bidder shall furnish _____ centrifuge(s) or _____ purifier(s) for cleaning or filtering of lubricating oil at a temperature of _____ F, (this) (these) to be of _____ make, or equal. (This) (these) unit(s) shall be for (continuous) (batch) purification of lubricating oil as follows:

_____ unit(s) for use with Item No. 1 (a), to have a capacity of approximately _____ gal per hour (each).
_____ unit(s) for use with Item No. 1 (b), to have a capacity of approximately _____ gal per hour (each).
_____ unit(s) for use with Item No. 1 (c), to have a capacity of approximately _____ gal per hour (each).

Alternate proposals based upon the engine manufacturer's or equipment manufacturer's recommendations will be considered. (The) (Each) unit shall be of vapor tight construction and shall be equipped with such used and clean oil pumps, electric or other type heaters, pressure gages, thermometers and controls as may be required for operation from 3-phase, 60-cycle, 220-volt current. Heater, if used, shall have automatic temperature control, and may be built-in or arranged for separate wall or floor mounting. If heater other than electric is used, steam (hot water) will be available at _____ psi (_____ F temperature). One complete change of filter materials or cells shall be furnished with each purifier requiring them.

---

* Buyers may wish both engine- and motor-driven units for large plants.

The successful bidder shall furnish a schematic drawing showing the proper connection of this equipment to the engine lubricating oil system. The successful bidder shall furnish data applying to the equipment offered on the equipment data form attached to these specifications.

> (Several variations of this specification suggest themselves. One centrifuge for as many as three similar engines may be specified, but this unit should be furnished with interlocking connections to engines so that oil cannot be transferred from one unit to another. If no heaters are to be used, the specification should so state, and bidders will then offer larger centrifuges or purifiers. It is recommended that engineers consult centrifuge or purifier specialists for suggestions.)

(h) Fuel Oil Centrifuge.[1]—The successful bidder shall furnish a fuel-oil centrifuge set, of _____ make, or equal, including centrifuge and motor, clean- and dirty-oil pumps, all mounted on a common base, motor to be equipped with starting switch, and to be suitable for three phase, 60-cycle, 220-volt current. The centrifuge shall be of vapor tight construction and suitable for handling _____ gal per hour of (distillate) (blended) (residual) (crude) oil at _____ F, _____ SSU, _____ percent water and sediment, _____ percent sulfur, _____° API. The successful bidder shall also furnish a closed oil heater for (steam at _____ lb pressure) (hot water at _____ F), such heater to be of a capacity to heat fuel at the foregoing rate in gallons per hour from _____ F to the temperature specified in the foregoing, and shall have thermostatic control to maintain this temperature. The dirty-oil pump shall be capable of a suction lift of _____ ft of oil; the clean-oil pump shall be capable of a discharge pressure of _____ psi. Each bidder shall furnish data applying to the fuel centrifuging equipment offered on the equipment data form attached to these specifications.

(i) Exhaust-Heat Boiler (Water Heater).[2]—The successful bidder shall furnish an (exhaust-heat boiler) (water heater) for (the) (each) engine of Item No. 1. (The) (Each) (boiler) (heater) shall be of _____ make, or equal, and shall have a capacity to utilize the exhaust of the (corresponding) engine for the (heating of water from _____ F to _____ F[3]) (raising of steam at _____ psi pressure from feed water at _____ F[3]). Suitable provision for feeding the (boiler[s]) (heater[s]) shall be made. The (boiler[s]) (heater[s]) (is) (are) to be designed and constructed in accordance with the latest ASME Standards, and _____ inspection agency. (Other regulations which apply are _____, copies of which are attached). (The) (Each) (boiler) (heater) shall be equipped with companion flanges, safety valve, pressure

---

[1] This equipment is ordinarily not needed. It is advisable to consult a centrifugal specialist if centrifuging of fuel oil is contemplated.

[2] Most plants can obtain heat for the power house and for lubricating oil treatment through use of less elaborate equipment.

Exhaust gases should not be cooled below the dew point; see page 50.

gage, water gage, try cocks and fittings and shall be furnished f.o.b. builder's work with freight allowed to siding. Each bidder shall furnish data applying to the (boiler[s]) (heater[s]) offered on the equipment data form attached to these specifications.

(j) Combination Exhaust Heat Boiler (Water Heater) and Exhaust Silencer.—An exhaust heat boiler and silencer may be combined and furnished in a single unit, in which case specifications as outlined under paragraphs (b) and (i) will apply.

(k) Fuel Oil Service Tank(s).—The successful bidder shall furnish a fuel-oil service tank for (the) (each) engine of Item No. 1, this to be of the engine builder's standard design and capacity. (The) (Each) tank shall be equipped with a level indicator. Fuel outlet(s) and by-pass(es) (if used) to the engine(s) shall be of the same size as the fuel connections to the (corresponding) engine. The tank(s) and bracket(s) shall be furnished f.o.b. the builder's works with freight allowed to siding. Each bidder shall furnish data applying to the fuel service tank(s) offered on the equipment data form attached to these specifications.

(l) Fuel Oil Transfer Pump.—The successful bidder shall furnish one (motor-driven) (hand-operated) fuel transfer pump of a capacity of approximately _____ gpm and for _____ ft suction lift, _____ ft total head, of (rotary) (reciprocating) type, (complete with motor and starting switch, motor for three phase, 60-cycle, 220-volt current). Each bidder shall supply data applying to the transfer pump offered on the equipment data form attached to these specifications.

(m) Raw and Jacket Water Pump(s).—The successful bidder shall furnish raw and jacket water pump(s), _____
(Number)
each, which shall be horizontal, single-stage, centrifugal pumps, of _____ make or equal, each double suction, with bronze impeller and bronze- shaft sleeves extending beyond the stuffing boxes. Each pump is to be furnished with a driving motor with starter, for 3-phase, 60-cycle, 220-volt current; each pump and motor shall be mounted on a common substantial base and shall be connected by a flexible coupling. The raw-water pump(s) shall have a capacity of _____ gpm when operating against _____ ft total head, including _____ ft suction (lift) (head). The jacket-water pump(s) shall have a capacity of _____ gpm when operating against a total head of _____ ft, including _____ ft suction (lift) (head). Each pump shall be complete with companion flanges. Each bidder shall furnish data applying to the pumps offered on the equipment data form attached to these specifications. Each pump and motor complete, mounted on the base, shall be furnished f.o.b. the pump builder's works with freight allowed to the siding.

(n) Shell and Tube Type Jacket Water Heat Exchangers. —The successful bidder shall furnish a shell and tube type heat

exchanger for (the) (each) engine of Item No. 1 to cool _____
gpm of engine jacket water from _____ F to _____ F when supplied with _____ gpm of raw water (specify source and conditions)
entering at _____ F and leaving at _____ F. The heat exchanger
is to be furnished f.o.b. the builder's works, with freight allowed
to the siding. Each bidder shall furnish data applying to the
exchanger furnished on the equipment data form attached to these
specifications.

(o) Alarms for Cooling Water and Lubricating Oil.—
The successful bidder shall furnish an audible or visible alarm
system (or both) for (the) (each) engine of Item No. 1, to be
operated on any failure of lubricating oil pressure, or increase in
circulating water temperature above that recommended by the
engine manufacturer, or any failure of the electric current energizing the alarm system. (Buyer shall specify source of current supply
for energizing alarm system, and related equipment desired.) This
equipment is to be furnished f.o.b. the builder's works with freight
allowed to the siding.

> (If automatic fuel shut-off devices, actuated by failure of lubri-
> cating oil pressure or high temperature of circulating water,
> are wanted, the specification should be inserted here along the
> foregoing lines.)

(p) Foundations.—Certified setting plans for all equipment
of this Item No. 3 requiring foundations are to be submitted by the
successful bidder after the signing of the contract. Foundation bolts
will be furnished by the successful bidder and foundations will be
designed and constructed by others.

Item 4:

Piping, Valves and Fittings.—The successful bidder shall
furnish all piping, valves and fittings in accordance with plans and
as described below, f.o.b. the builder's works with freight allowed to
the siding, for (a) fuel oil within the power house, (b) lubricating
oil, (c) starting air, (d) engine air inlet(s) and (e) engine ex-
haust(s), but not for fuel oil or fuel oil heater outside the power
house, or for the cooling water system, which will be furnished by
others. This Item also does not include any piping, valves or fittings
which are a part of the engine(s) and auxiliaries covered in Items
No. 1 and No. 3. (Item No. 4 is usually supplied by the buyer
except exhaust and intake piping which are often supplied by the
bidder.)

(a) Station Fuel Oil Piping furnished shall connect to such
piping furnished under Section No. 4 and shall include a _____ in.
line to the transfer pump (which is furnished under Item No. 3),
a _____ in. line from this pump to (the) (each) service tank, a line
of the size required by (the) (each) engine from (the) (each)
service tank to the (corresponding) engine, a by-pass line (if

required) from (the) (each) engine to the (corresponding) service tank, an overflow line two sizes larger than the filling line, from (the) (each) service tank to the storage tank. A fuel oil strainer shall be included in the supply line to the service tank(s). All fuel oil piping shall be full-weight iron or steel, if pickled on the inside and blown free from scale, or may be copper or brass. Connections shall not depend upon gaskets or joint cement affected by fuel oil.

(b) Station Lubricating Oil Piping shall be full-weight pipe or equivalent. Gaskets, if used, shall be of a material not affected by lubricating oil.

(c) Starting Air Piping, Valves and Fittings shall be suitable for the starting air pressure recommended for the engine(s) of Item No. 1.

(d) Piping for (the) (each) Engine Air Inlet shall be suitable for an inlet system similar to that shown in Figs. 7, 8 or 9, DEMA Standard Practices. Exact locations for the engine(s) and inlet piping are shown in the plans attached. Inlet-air piping shall be of _____.

(e) Exhaust Piping shall be_____

_____

_____

(f) General.—All power plant piping shall be provided with flexible connections and expansion joints where required. All piping shall be adequately supported and braced to avoid vibration and possible fatigue.

Item 5:

Labor.—The buyer will furnish all labor, equipment and gear required to erect and install the equipment, including machinery, auxiliaries, piping, etc., specified in this Section No. 1, under the supervision of the erecting engineer included in Item No. 1, including the rigging of machinery from a receiving place adjacent to the power house and within the grounds of the site, into place on foundations constructed by others.

Section 2

Switchgear, Cables, Conduits, Etc.
(Usually not included in Engine Contract)

Item 1:

The Switchboard to be furnished in accordance with detailed specifications as follows _____

_____

The successful bidder shall furnish the services of an erecting engineer to superintend the installation and placing in service of the switchboard and electrical apparatus of this Section. The switchboard and transformers are to be furnished f.o.b. the builder's works with freight allowed to the siding. Each bidder shall state the make of switchboard offered and shall list all equipment mounted thereon by name and by the catalog number of the builder, this data to be presented on the equipment data form attached to these specifications.

Item 2:

Cables and Conduits shall be furnished to connect (a) (the) (each) generator and exciter to the (respective) generator panel, (b) the station panel to all motor-driven auxiliaries, and (c) cables and conduits for engine pyrometer equipment and engine alarms. For all other cables and conduits see Section 7. All cables are to be located (in conduits, such conduits to be also furnished) (on racks in covered trenches, such racks to be also furnished) (overhead, including supports), are to be in accordance with the latest standards of the NBFU and the NEMA for service intended, and shall be installed in accordance with the same. All cables and conduits are to be furnished f.o.b. the builder's works with freight allowed to the siding.

Item 3:

Additional Electrical Equipment shall be furnished as follows:

Item 4:

The Successful Bidder Shall Furnish all labor, equipment and gear to install and place in service the equipment, including switchboard, cables and conduit, etc., specified in this Section No. 2, under supervision of the erecting engineer included in Item No. 1, Section 2, including the rigging of equipment into place from a receiving place adjacent to the power house and within the grounds of the site.

Section 3

Cooling Water System
(Usually not included in Engine Contract)

(It is impossible to cover all cooling systems in a generalized specification such as this. What follows applies to a typical recommended system (Fig. 17); buyers can easily modify this text to suit other recommended systems.)

Item 1:

Cooling Tower(s), Atmospheric or Induced Draft, shall be furnished, to cool _____ gpm[1] from _____ F to _____ F with an average wind velocity of _____ miles per hour, prevailing from the _____ direction and with a mean high daily dry bulb temperature of _____ F and wet bulb temperature of _____ F in the month of _____, the hottest month of the year at the site. The tower is to be for installation on a concrete sump as covered in Section 7, and is for use in connection with an atmospheric-type heat exchanger as specified in Item No. 2 of Section 3. The tower shall be constructed of (cypress) (redwood) (cedar) (steel) and shall be internally braced to withstand a wind of 100 miles per hour. The decks of the tower shall support a load of 30 lb per sq ft. A walkway along the distributing system at the top of the tower shall be supplied, together with a ladder from the ground level to the walkway. All nuts, bolts, and hardware not of cast iron shall be hot-dipped galvanized. All nails shall be of copper. A redistributing system shall be installed to distribute the water uniformly over the heat exchanger. All sprinklers and spray nozzles, if used, shall be of cast bronze. This Item includes also the services of an engineer to superintend the installation and placing in service of the tower and other parts of the cooling system. The tower shall be furnished f.o.b. the builder's works with freight allowed to the siding. Each bidder shall furnish data applying to the tower offered on the equipment data form attached to these specifications.

Item 2:

An Atmospheric-Type Heat Exchanger[2] shall be furnished to cool _____ gpm of soft water from _____ F to _____ F when operating with the cooling tower of Item No. 1 of this Section. This shall consist of _____ pipe with suitable headers, with supports necessary for mounting under the tower. Companion flanges shall be included. The exchanger is to be furnished f.o.b. the builder's works with freight allowed to the siding. Each bidder shall furnish data applying to the exchanger furnished on the equipment data form attached to these specifications. (If shell and tube type heat exchanger is to be furnished, this will be included in Section 1.)

Item 3:

One (1) Expansion and Make-up Water Tank shall be furnished with each system. The tank must have a capacity of at least _____ gal (approximately 50 percent in excess of the total expansion volume of the water in the engine cooling circuit). The tank should be vented to the atmosphere and have a sight gage or level

---

[1] Allow here for future unit, if contemplated.
[2] Shell and tube type heat exchangers are often supplied for jacket water cooling instead of atmospheric type, and evaporative coolers or radiators are also used.

meter to indicate the water level for the operator's convenience. The tank must be above the highest water level on the engine and must be connected to the highest engine outlet point, to the suction side of the circulating water pump and to a source of make-up water.

Item 4:

All Cooling Water System Piping, Valves and Fittings shown in the plans shall be furnished. Piping shall be _____ with (flanged) (screwed) fittings. All valves shall be brass-fitted, rising stem gate valves. Piping shall be of size and arrangement as shown by plans. Pump-suction openings in sumps shall be provided with strainers. The raw-water make-up valve shall be float operated. A water-pressure gage for 0-30 psi shall be provided for location as shown in the plans. All piping, valves and fittings shall be furnished f.o.b. the builder's works with freight allowed to the siding.

Item 5:

The Buyer Shall Furnish all labor, equipment and gear except as noted, required to install and place in service the equipment specified in Section No. 3, under the supervision of the erecting engineer included in Item No. 1, Section 1, including the rigging of equipment from a receiving place adjacent to the power house and within the grounds of the site, into place on foundations furnished under Section 7.

Section 4

Fuel Oil Storage System
(Usually not included in Engine Contract)

Item 1:

_____ **(Vertical) (Horizontal) Fuel-Oil Storage Tank(s)** shall be furnished, of not less than _____ gal cap. (each). (The) (Each) tank shall be approximately _____ ft (high) (long) and _____ ft in diameter. (The tank[s] shall be suitable for above-ground installations as shown in DEMA Standard Practices, Figs. 24 or 25.) (The tank[s] shall be for below-ground installations as shown in DEMA Standard Practices, Fig. 26, and shall be protected by asphaltum paint.) (The) (Each) tank(s) shall have openings as shown in DEMA Standard Practices, of the following sizes: (a) fuel inlet _____ in., (b) fuel outlet _____ in., (c) vent _____ in., (d) overflow from plant _____ in., (e) (hot-water) (steam) inlet and outlet _____ in., (f) drain (horizontal above-ground only) _____ in. (The) (Each) tank shall be constructed and installed in accordance with the latest rules of the NBFU (Local regulations applying to fuel-oil storage tanks are attached hereto in full.) (The) (Each) tank shall be suitable for mounting on concrete foundations as specified in Section 7. Tank connections shall be equipped with companion flanges. The tank(s) shall be furnished f.o.b. builder's works with freight allowed to siding. Each bidder shall furnish data applying to the tank(s) offered on the equipment data form attached to these specifications.

Item 2:

Fuel Oil Unloading Pump(s),[1] rotary type, shall be furnished complete with motor and starting switch, for 3-phase, 60-cycle, 220-volt current, each pump and motor to be mounted upon a substantial base. Each pump shall be for a capacity of not less than .... gpm when handling fuel oil of ....° API against a head of .... psi. Each pump shall be equipped with companion flanges. Each pump, motor and base shall be furnished f.o.b. the builder's works with freight allowed to the siding. Each bidder shall furnish data applying to the pump offered on the equipment data form attached to these specifications.

Item 3:

All Piping, Valves and Fittings for fuel-oil system, including heating system,[2] up to and including unions within the power house, shall be furnished in accordance with plans. All fuel-oil piping shall be full-weight iron, steel or other approved material. Connections shall not depend upon gaskets or joint cement affected by fuel oil. All valves, except quick acting valves shown in the plans, shall be rising stem gate valves, these to be all steel if located near above-ground tanks. A relief valve shall be furnished for the discharge line from the unloading pump. (If a buried tank is specified, there should be a foot valve for the end of the fuel suction within the tank.) The relative positions of the siding, unloading pump, fuel storage tank(s), power house, the location of all piping and valves are shown in the plans. All piping, valves and fittings are to be furnished f.o.b. the builder's works with freight allowed to the siding.

Item 4:

The Buyer Shall Furnish all labor, equipment and gear required to install and place in service all equipment of this Section No. 4, under the supervision of the erection engineer included in Item 1, Section 1, including the rigging of equipment from a receiving place adjacent to the power house and within the grounds of the site, into place, on foundations furnished under Section 7.

---

[1] If the siding is sufficiently elevated above the storage tanks, the fuel may be discharged by gravity.
[2] Such fuel-heating arrangements are required when heavy fuel oil is to be used, or in cold climates. The engine builder should be consulted for recommendations in such cases.

Section 5

Gaseous Fuel Storage and Handling System
(Usually not included in Engine Contract)

Item 1:

Scrubbers and/or settling chambers shall be supplied as required to furnish dry, clean gas of uniform quality. Pressure regulator shall be supplied as required to furnish gas at a pressure not exceeding 250 psi.

Item 2:

All piping, valves, and fittings for the gas system up to and including unions within the powerhouse shall be furnished in accordance with plans. All gas piping shall be full weight iron, steel, or other approved material. All valves shall be lubricated steel plug valves. All piping, valves, and fittings shall be furnished f.o.b. the builder's works with freight allowed to the siding.

Section 6

Unloading and Hauling
(Usually not included in Engine Contract)

The successful bidder shall furnish all labor, equipment and gear (except that furnished by the buyer and itemized elsewhere in the specifications) to unload all equipment of Sections No. 1 to 4 inclusive from cars at the siding and haul the same to, and unload at, a receiving place on the site. The distance from the siding to the site is .... ft (or miles) and the best route includes ....

(list kind and length of various roadways and rights of way)
Bridges to be traversed are .... The
(list type and weight limits)
minimum head-room on the route is .... ft from road-level and occurs at ....

(In some cases the buyer may wish to subcontract the moving of equipment in Section 1 to 4 from the receiving place on the site to the foundations, and if so, this specification should be so amended.)

Section 7
Power-Plant Building
(Usually not included in Engine Contract)

Specifications for this Section should include provisions for the following:

Excavation.
Footings.
Concrete walls.
Concrete floors.
Steel framing.
Brickwork, concrete blocks or other types of siding.
Sash.
Doors.
Windows.
Roof, including waterproofing.
Foundations for—
    Engines and auxiliaries.
    Cooling system equipment.
    Fuel system equipment.
    Lubricating oil system equipment.
Bolts for all foundations except those otherwise provided.
Trenches and covers.
Muffler (pits) (supports).
Air filter mountings.
Lights, fixtures and wiring to switchgear.
Plumbing and toilet facilities, including piping and fittings for same.
Heating system, with all piping and fittings but not including boiler (if exhaust-gas boiler has been specified elsewhere).
Ventilating system.
Hoists, or crane and runway, including all wiring to switchboard (if hoists are electric).
Guards and railings for generator units and any other equipment to be protected.

EQUIPMENT DATA FORM
(Information to be supplied by the Bidder)
Section 1

Item 1: Engine(s)

	Unit 1	Unit 2	Unit 3
Make of engine(s):	....	....	....
Type of engine(s):			
Two- or four-cycle?	....	....	....
Supercharged or non-supercharged?	....	....	....
Type of supercharging (if used)	....	....	....

	Unit 1	Unit 2	Unit 3
Air or mechanical injection?	....	....	....
Oil, Dual Fuel or Gas?	....	....	....
Means for providing scavenging air, if two-cycle	....	....	....
Means for providing injection air (if air injection)	....	....	....
Single-acting, double-acting, or opposed piston?	....	....	....
Trunk piston or crosshead?	....	....	....
Are pistons cooled?	....	....	....
If so, by oil or water?	....	....	....
Arrangement of cylinders (In-line, V or ....)	....	....	....

Size of engine(s):

	Unit 1	Unit 2	Unit 3
Number of power cylinders.	....	....	....
Bore, in.	....	....	....
Stroke, in.	....	....	....
Rated speed, rpm	....	....	....
Piston speed, ft.p.m.	....	....	....
Standard sea-level rating, bhp	....	....	....
Altitude at site, ft	....	....	....
Rating at altitude of the site, and ambient temperature of .... F, DEMA Standard Practices, bhp	....	....	....
Rated bmep at site	....	....	....

Dimensions and Data:

	Unit 1	Unit 2	Unit 3
Overall width, without platform, ft	....	....	....
Overall width, with platform, ft	....	....	....
Overall height from floor-level, ft	....	....	....
Overall height from floor to bottom of crane hook to pull piston and rod assembly, ft	....	....	....
Height of crankshaft center-line above floor, ft	....	....	....
Overall length, with generator and (direct connected) (belted) exciter, ft	....	....	....

	Unit 1	Unit 2	Unit 3

Approximate foundation required (each) engine, generator, and exciter for good soil, cu yd

Weight Data:

Shipping weight of engine, less flywheel, lb

Shipping weight of flywheel, lb

Shipping weight of engine(s), flywheel(s) and equipment as furnished under Sec. 1, lb

Shipping weight of heaviest piece to be handled, lb

Weight of heaviest piece to be handled in normal maintenance, lb

Fuel consumption, according to DEMA Standard Practices at site, using fuel complying with bidder's specifications:

Oil Operation,

Pounds of Fuel per bhp-hr:
@ 4/4 Load, _____ bhp
@ 3/4 Load, _____ bhp
@ 1/2 Load, _____ bhp

Dual Fuel, Gas Operation,

Total Gas (lhv) and Pilot Oil (hhv) Btu per bhp-hr.
@ 4/4 Load, _____ bhp
@ 3/4 Load, _____ bhp
@ 1/2 Load, _____ bhp

Pilot Oil, Btu per bhp-hr. (hhv) (Included in above total)

@ 4/4 Load, _____ bhp
@ 3/4 Load, _____ bhp
@ 1/2 Load, _____ bhp

Gas Operation,

Total Gas (lhv)
@ 4/4 Load, _____ bhp
@ 3/4 Load, _____ bhp
@ 1/2 Load, _____ bhp

(lhv means low heat value; hhv means high heat value)

	Unit 1	Unit 2	Unit 3
Miscellaneous Engine Data:			
List of spare parts included (bidder may attach separate list)	....	....	....
Type of barring device (hand, pneumatic or electric)	....	....	....
Type of lubrication of main parts of engine(s)	....	....	....
Cylinder lubrication (splash or force-feed)	....	....	....
Air storage pressure for starting, psi	....	....	....
Cooling water quantity required to maintain .... F temperature difference as recommended by manufacturer between inlet to and outlet from engine, gpm	....	....	....
Maximum cooling water temperature recommended at full load, F	....	....	....
Pressure drop through engine headers and jackets, and oil coolers (if furnished) for water circulation rate recommended, feet of water	....	....	....
Lubricating oil quantity required to maintain .... F temperature difference as recommended by manufacturer between inlet to and outlet from engine, gpm	....	....	....
Maximum lubricating oil temperature recommended at full load, F	....	....	....
Engine shipping promise(s) in weeks	....	....	....

Item 2: Generator(s) and Exciter(s)

Make of generator(s)			
Full load rating, at ...... percent power factor, at elevation of site, kw	....	....	....

	Unit 1	Unit 2	Unit 3
Engine, flywheel or bracket type?	....	....	....
Rated speed of generator(s), rpm	....	....	....
Size of exciter(s), kw	....	....	....
Exciter(s) direct connected or belted?	....	....	....
Rated speed of exciter(s), rpm	....	....	....
Efficiencies of generator(s) at rated power factor of ___ %, in accordance with NEMA Standards:*			
100% load, kw	....	....	....
Efficiency %	....	....	....
75% load, kw	....	....	....
Efficiency %	....	....	....
50% load, kw	....	....	....
Efficiency %	....	....	....
Shipping weights, lb	....	....	....
Generator(s) (with) (without) engine extension shaft(s)	....	....	....
Exciter(s)	....	....	....
Generator and exciter shipping promise(s) in weeks	....	....	....

Item 3: Auxiliaries

(a) Pyrometer Equipment

	Unit 1	Unit 2	Unit 3
Make of Equipment	....	....	....
Where installed	....	....	....
Number of switch points, (each instrument)	....	....	....

(b) Exhaust Muffler(s)

	Unit 1	Unit 2	Unit 3
Make and model	....		
Size number	....	....	....
Shipping weight, lb	....	....	....

(c) Intake-Air Muffler(s)

	Unit 1	Unit 2	Unit 3
Make and model	....		
Size number	....	....	....
Shipping weight, lb	....	....	....

---

* When it is necessary to make tests at other than normal rating of kilowatts, power factor, speed or voltage, the generator efficiency at such test condiions shall be determined from data to be furnished by the generator manufacturer.

	Unit 1	Unit 2	Unit 3

(d) Air Filter(s)

Make and model

Type

Shipping weight, lb

(e) Starting Air Plant

Bhp of compressor (engine) (motor)

Rated rpm of (engine) (motor)

Actual free air capacity, cfm

Rated rpm of compressor

Number of air tanks furnished

Size (of each), diameter and overall length or height

Maximum working tank pressure, psi

Approximate number of starts per engine per tank

Shipping weight of compressor, (engine) (motor), and common base, lb

Shipping weight of (each) tank, lb

(f) Lubricating Oil Centrifuge(s) or Purifier(s)

Make

Size or model number

Rated capacity, gph

Operation, continuous or batch

Type heater (electric, steam or hot water)

Rating of heater, if electric, kw

Total rating of motors, if used, hp

Maximum suction lift of used oil pump, if used, ft

Method of cleaning, centrifuging or filtering

Filtering medium, if used (disc, fibrous or earth)

Number of cells

Size of cells

Shipping weight complete, each unit, lb

	Unit 1	Unit 2	Unit 3

(g) Fuel Oil Centrifuge(s) or Purifier(s)

	Unit 1	Unit 2	Unit 3
Make			
Size or model number			
Rated capacity, gph			
Operation, continuous or batch			
Type heater (electric, steam or hot water)			
Rating of heater, if electric, kw			
Total rating of motors, if used, hp			
Maximum suction lift of fuel oil pump, if used, ft			
Method of cleaning, centrifuging or filtering			
Filtering medium, if used (disc, fibrous or earth)			
Number of cells			
Size of cells			
Shipping weight complete, each unit, lb			

(h) Exhaust Heat Boiler(s) or Combination Boiler(s) and Silencer(s)

	Unit 1	Unit 2	Unit 3
Make			
Size number and model			
Diameter, ft			
Height (length), ft			
Square ft of heating surface			
Approximate capacity in lb of steam per hour, at _____ psi pressure at exhaust-gas temperature corresponding to _____ load on engine			
Approximate capacity to raise _____lb of water from _____ F to _____ F with _____ load on engine			
Shipping weight, lb			

(i) Fuel Service Tank

	Unit 1	Unit 2	Unit 3
Capacity, gal			
Dimensions			
Type of level indicator			
Shipping weight, lb			

	Unit 1	Unit 2	Unit 3

(j) Fuel Transfer Pump

Make ....
Capacity, gpm ....
Rating of motor, bhp ....
Type (rotary, reciprocating, etc.) ....
Shipping weight, lb ....

(k) Jacket Water Pumps

Make of pump ....
Make of motor ....
Speed, rpm ....
Capacity at ...... tdh, gpm ....
Rating of motor, hp ....
Shipping weight of pump, motor and base, lb ....

(l) Raw Water Pumps

Make of pump ....
Make of motor ....
Speed, rpm ....
Capacity at ...... tdh, gpm ....
Rating of motor, hp ....
Shipping weight of pump, motor and base, lb ....

(m) Heat Exchanger, Shell and Tube Type*

Make and model ....
Friction loss, jacket water side, psi ....
Friction loss, raw water side, psi ....
Entering jacket water temperature, F ....
Leaving jacket water temperature, F ....
Entering raw water temperature, F ....
Leaving raw water temperature, F ....
Gpm jacket water ....
Gpm raw water ....
Shipping weight, lb ....

---

* Data on details of design are omitted as their effect on performance varies from time to time depending upon the state of the art of any given industry.

	Unit 1	Unit 2	Unit 3
(n) Lubricating Oil Cooler*			
Make and model	--------------	--------------	--------------
Friction loss, lubricating oil side, psi	--------------	--------------	--------------
Friction loss, water side, psi	--------------	--------------	--------------
Entering lubricating oil temperature, F	--------------	--------------	--------------
Leaving lubricating oil temperature, F	--------------	--------------	--------------
Entering water temperature, F	--------------	--------------	--------------
Leaving water temperature, F	--------------	--------------	--------------
Gpm lubricating oil	--------------	--------------	--------------
Gpm water	--------------	--------------	--------------
Shipping weight, lb	--------------	--------------	--------------

Section 2

Item 1:   Switchgear

Make and model   --

Catalogue Numbers and
Descriptions

Equipment on each generator
panel:

Equipment on each feeder
panel:

Equipment on station (auxiliary) panel:

---

* See footnote page 193.

	Unit 1	Unit 2	Unit 3
Other equipment:	------	------	------
	------	------	------
	------	------	------
	------	------	------

Section 3

Item 1: Cooling Tower

	Unit 1	Unit 2	Unit 3
Make of tower	------	------	------
Water loss, in percent of circulation	------	------	------
Type of distributing system, top of tower	------	------	------
Type of distributing system for heat exchanger	------	------	------
Total pumping head for rated capacity, ft	------	------	------
Heat dissipations, based on conditions specified under Item 1, Sec. 3 of Specifications, p. 182, Btu/hr	------	------	------
Overall dimensions, height from foundations, ft	------	------	------
Width, ft	------	------	------
Depth, ft	------	------	------
Shipping weight, lb	------	------	------

Item 2: Tank and Tower

	Unit 1	Unit 2	Unit 3
Make of tower	------	------	------
Make of tank	------	------	------
Height of tank, ft	------	------	------
Diameter of tank, ft	------	------	------
Type of water-level alarm	------	------	------
Shipping weight of tower, lb	------	------	------
Shipping weight of tank, lb	------	------	------

Section 4

Item 1: Heavy Oil Fuel Storage Tank(s)

	Unit 1	Unit 2	Unit 3
Make of tank(s)	------	------	------
Dimensions (length) (height), ft	------	------	------
Diameter, ft	------	------	------
Capacity, gal	------	------	------
Shipping weight, lb	------	------	------

	Unit 1	Unit 2	Unit 3

Item 2: Light Oil Fuel Storage Tank(s)

Make of tank(s)
Dimensions (length) (height), ft
Diameter, ft
Capacity, gal
Shipping weight, lb

Item 3: Fuel Oil Unloading Pump

Make of pump
Make of motor
Speed of pump and motor, rpm
Rating of motor, bhp
Shipping weight, complete, lb

Lea County Electric Co-op at Lovington, New Mexico, operates four 18 by 27 and three 16 by 20 two-cycle dual fuel engines.

CHAPTER TWENTY

Operation and Maintenance

When taking charge of an engine, an operator should first become acquainted with the location and function of its parts. In the case of newly purchased engines of appreciable size, it is frequently desirable for an owner to have his chief engineer visit the engine builder's plant while the engine is being erected. If this is not practical, the engine builder's field representative can be of assistance in familiarizing the operators with the engine. The manufacturer's instructions and parts lists are particularly useful in this connection.

There are usually several ways of laying out the starting, cooling water, fuel, lubricating oil, air intake and exhaust systems to accomplish the purpose intended. An operator should familiarize himself with the purpose of each pipe, valve, fitting and mechanical or electrical accessory used in all parts of his installation. This can be accomplished by analyzing each system from its source. In the case of the fuel system, for example, the piping may be traced from the main storage tank, determining the reason for each fitting in the route which the fuel must follow before reaching the engine.

After acquiring a knowledge of the layout of each system, it is desirable in the case of new installations or those which have been idle some time, that before starting, an operator test out all fuel, lubricating oil and water lines, to see that they are tight and internally clear. Air should be purged from the liquid systems through vents at the highest point while filling or circulating the liquid. Air starting piping can be blown free of foreign matter, after removing strainers in the lines, by disconnecting the air line at the engine and applying the full working pressure of the air tank at the other end. In this way the line can blow into the open to free any loose pieces of pipe scale, joint cement, small chips, parts of gaskets, etc.

The engine should then be barred over by hand a few revolutions to insure there are no restrictions. After other necessary preparations preliminary to starting have been made, and the engine started, it should be run at a speed as low as practical while observing all gages. The engine speed should be increased gradually while observing pressures and temperatures, to make sure all parts are working properly.

Manufacturers issue specific instructions for each of their engines and such instructions are the result of wide experience. To secure the utmost in reliability and efficiency, these instructions should be read, understood and followed. The information given in this chapter is not intended in any way to supersede any such instructions, but rather to point out the desirability of following them. However, engine instruction books are largely confined to a description of the engine itself and this chapter is therefore devoted to coordinating the various external systems involved.

It should be appreciated that cleanliness is an absolute necessity, particularly in relation to the fuel and lubricating oil systems. A large number of delays and repairs result from neglect of this fundamental truth. Engines may stop unexpectedly due to no other cause than a clogged filter.

All well managed power plants have much in common. At a glance, one is impressed with the cleanliness of the engines, auxiliaries and engine room floor and evident care and attention that has been given to all power plant equipment. It is apparent from the clean, well kept appearance of such plants that the operators are inspired by a high sense of duty. Each attendant is obviously proud of his share in the result. Total operating economy of an engine includes the cost of fuel, lubricating oil, repairs, engine attendance and the cost of delays, if any, chargeable to machinery repairs. An important controlling factor is thoroughness. It has been frequently demonstrated that a certain type of machinery may be operated with great success by one set of engine operators, while the same equipment in other hands may prove troublesome. Such a condition suggests the importance of proper machinery care and operation, and what follows includes some of the more important considerations in this respect.

Upon arrival at the plant, all spares should be carefully checked, inspected, properly protected from rust, identified with tags or other means, and placed in storage. A skillful initial arrangement of tools and spares can be invaluable to the operating personnel in making adjustments and repairs when needed. When spare parts are used, they should be reordered so that a complete set may be kept available.

Arrangements should also be made for the assembly of all pertinent machinery information, suitably indexed and carefully bound. Copies of the material should be made available to all responsible operating personnel.

Manufacturers' instruction books give detailed procedure to be followed in starting, stopping, and running; also necessary information on capacities, clearances, pressures and temperatures, together with required particulars for disassembly, adjustment and reassembly of the parts involved. Good plant management requires adoption of routine inspection and cleaning of the various parts indicated by the manufacturer's instructions at intervals recommended by them. These recommended intervals should be adhered to until experience gained through subsequent operation clearly demonstrates some other schedule better suited to the requirements of the installation in question.

Power Plant Log.—All well managed power plants maintain engine room logs. This practice is always recommended. The form of log depends upon the operating conditions and the characteristics of the equipment used. Operating conditions vary greatly between different types of plants, and this tends to make it difficult if not practically impossible to set up here a maintenance schedule that will apply to all installations. It is possible, however, to establish a fixed maintenance schedule for a particular type of equipment when the operating conditions are thoroughly known. It is accordingly desirable that the owner's representative consult with the manufacturers of his engines in the event a form of log is not already available.

The log should have provision for recording the starting and stopping time of each engine, the loads and such pressures and temperatures as can be secured with the instruments available. Fuel and lubricating oil consumptions, and, if possible, the daily power output, should be recorded for each unit. A liberal space may be devoted on such a log to remarks, and in this space, notation made of anything which indicates some attention necessary to a part, whether at the time of entry, or at some future time. These logs are usually based on a 24 hour operating period and provide space for each of the shift engineers to sign for the readings taken during his watch. It is obvious that if these logs are maintained daily covering each engine, they will provide an invaluable record of the performance of the engines and of all maintenance made or needed.

It should be remembered that any appreciable change from normal operating temperatures and pressures without a corresponding change in load is worth investigating. It may be a signal that some part requires attention. A carefully kept log will show the gradual changes from day to day and, by comparison with previous readings, will enable an operator to determine in advance, the necessity for each routine maintenance procedure recommended by the manufacturer. Without such a guide before him, an operator is apt to undertake some maintenance work sooner than necessary, while at the same time overlook other items more essential to continued economical performance.

Fuel Oil Systems.—Fuel oil systems including tanks should be checked periodically for presence of water and sediment. Where pressure gages are installed before and after the filter, an abnormal pressure differential will indicate the need for cleaning of the filter elements or replacement of the filter cartridges. Where such gages are not used, the condition of the filter must be determined by periodic inspection. Strainers should also be periodically inspected.

Adjustments to the injection equipment should not be made by anyone who is not sufficiently familiar with it, and it is always advisable not to take down more than a small section at a time to preclude confusion in reassembly. In breaking connections of fuel lines which are to be exposed for any appreciable period, the free ends should be carefully covered to prevent entrance of foreign matter. The work space utilized in servicing or repairing injection equipment should be thoroughly cleaned before disassembly of any injection system parts. No other work which might produce dirt or abrasive particles should be allowed to proceed in the immediate area. The manufacturer supplies specific instructions for each piece of injection equipment and these should be carefully observed.

Gaseous Fuel Systems.—Gaseous fuel systems must be clean because abrasives are harmful to the regulating equipment and the engine. Where gas cleaners or strainers are used, the condition of this equipment should be checked periodically.

If a booster gas compressor is used, instructions on maintenance of this equipment are generally furnished by the supplier and should be carefully followed. Oil separators are frequently supplied with gas compressors and a periodic check should be made on the oil drains on these separators to be sure they are draining properly.

Lubricating Systems.—When a lubricating oil filter becomes clogged, an engine may either suffer from lack of oil or be supplied with dirty oil. In either case bearings may be ruined before the trouble is located. Before starting a new installation, the entire lubrication system, including all oil lines, oil coolers, strainers, filters and supply and sump tanks should be thoroughly cleaned to insure freedom from filings, chips, welding shot and other foreign matter.

Lubricating oil filters and strainers should be cleaned and inspected at regular intervals. Gages should be provided on both inlet and outlet sides, and observation of undue pressure differentials will indicate the necessity for cleaning or renewal of filter elements. Engine crank pits and lubricating oil sump tanks should be inspected and cleaned of sludge periodically.

Symptoms such as abnormal engine sounds or smells, unaccountable speed changes, or unusual temperature and pressure readings should suggest the desirability for prompt investigation, and, where necessary, the engine should be stopped as soon as practicable. The circulation of lubricating oil and cooling water should be continued long enough after the engine has been stopped to allow it to cool before any of the access covers are removed.

Necessary inspection and correction should precede further operation of the engine. It is good practice not to remove crankcase doors or other access covers from hot engines until they have cooled for at least 10 minutes after stopping to avoid the possibility of explosion of hot crankcase vapors mixing with fresh air. This is particularly true where any moving parts have been running considerably above normal temperatures. No open lights should be put in the crankcase at this time.

If both an engine and its supply of lubricant are cold, the engine should be started slowly and the gages watched carefully to make sure the lubricant is circulating freely before increasing engine speed or load. Temperatures recommended by the engine manufacturer should be observed and followed.

Lubricating oil should be changed when necessary. The length of time will vary with grade of lubricating oil, fuel oil, load, condition of engine and the care given it, along with temperatures of oil and water. Various tests with proper equipment can help determine when oil needs changing, and some oil companies can and will furnish this service.

Small engines using small quantities of oil in the lubricating oil system usually require that the oil be changed after a certain number of hours operation. Large quantities of oil should not be discarded without testing them for acidity, viscosity and dirt.

With proper filter equipment, acidity and cleanliness can be controlled, but viscosity cannot. Heavier oils, when used for cylinder lubrication, tend to raise viscosity. Fuel oil dilution in the lubricating oil lowers its viscosity.

Oil put into a new engine, or one that has been thoroughly cleaned down to the metal, will become acid rapidly and should be put through proper filters or be changed after a short period of time. The rate of acidity will diminish to normal after the oil system has become well coated or "seasoned." Make-up should be added to the system in small quantities (about 10 percent of full amount in system) and then circulated with the engine operating at normal temperature for some time before putting in more, otherwise there is danger of the new oil not mixing properly. This can happen with new and old oils of the same grade, and it is apt to happen if they are of different grades. Detergent oils should never be mixed with straight mineral or other detergent oils unless approved by the oil vendor.

Cooling Water Systems.—Cooling water temperatures can indicate the extent of cooling only if the cooling surfaces are free from scale and the cooling spaces properly filled with coolant. Indirect or closed systems employing jacket water coolers have two separate circuits. If any of the water spaces of either circuit are covered by a coating of scale or mud, this coating acts as an insulator in preventing transfer of heat to the coolant. Since the jacket water is subjected to temperatures which may accelerate corrosion and deposit of scale, both makeup and jacket water should be periodically tested and treated where necessary to insure that they are clean and free from harmful alkalies or acids. The system should be initially filled with soft or treated water. Engine jacket water spaces as well as jacket water coolers should be inspected periodically. Precautions should be taken to see that centrifugal pumps are primed and that suction connections are airtight. Coolers should be checked and inspected for leaks. Distilled or rain water should not be used without treatment to prevent corrosion.

If water circulation fails for any reason, and the engine overheats, the engine should be shut down as soon as practicable and cold water should not be admitted to the system until the jacketed surfaces have cooled to approximately the inlet water temperature to avoid unequal strains and fracture. Checking of temperature on the raw water side of the cooler or the pressure differential between the inlet and outlet of the cooler will indicate when the tubes require cleaning. If the discharge from the raw water side of the jacket water cooler is cold while the engine becomes hot, it is an indication that the raw water is not carrying away the heat properly.

Air Intake and Exhaust Systems.—Air intake and exhaust systems must be clean and unrestricted, otherwise an engine may be harmed by abrasives, or unable to carry a normal load either due to lack of sufficient air for combustion or because of excessive exhaust back-pressure. Intake air filters are recommended and should be inspected regularly and cleaned in accordance with the recommended schedule of the manufacturer. Exhaust lines, including exhaust mufflers, should be kept free from carbon, and dust collector boxes, where provided, should be inspected and cleaned periodically.

Starting Air Systems.—Starting air systems require scheduled inspection and attention. A frequent cause of trouble can be excess moisture in the starting air. Expansion of starting air from the air receivers to the engine cylinders will tend to condense excess moisture in the engine, resulting in corrosion of air valves, emulsification of lubricating oil and pitting of internally lubricated surfaces. Starting air receivers, and after-coolers where used, should be drained of water regularly. Where more than one starting air receiver is installed, it is desirable to maintain one of the receivers fully charged for emergency use, while starting from the other receiver or receivers. The starting air compressors, controls and air valves should be regularly inspected and maintained in the manner called for by the manufacturers of such equipment.

Electric Systems.—Motors, generators, contactors, switches and electrical starting equipment should be kept clean and in proper working order. All electrical connections should be kept tight. Batteries, if used, should be kept fully charged and filled with water to the proper level. Only distilled water should be added to the batteries.

Generators and Exciters.—The successful operation of the generators and exciters depends to a large extent on the degree of maintenance. This is particularly true of the insulation, which should be kept free from dirt, oil, grease, moisture and other contaminators. Periodic inspection, cleaning, revarnishing where necessary and megger testing will materially aid in prolonging the insulation life and preventing failures resulting in extensive damage. The stator ducts and coil interstices should be kept clean to prevent plugging up with dirt and restricting the flow of ventilating air, which results in overheating of the windings.

Alignment.—Alignment of the engine crankshaft and driven equipment, for any type of engine drive, is essential and should be checked periodically in accordance with the manufacturer's instructions.

Repairs.—Repairs should be made in an orderly manner. It should be observed how parts are put together before they are disassembled and, if necessary, marks made so as to facilitate returning the various parts to the exact positions.

In replacing any bolted parts, all nuts or tap bolts should be set up hand-tight, after which one nut should be wrench-tightened slightly, then a nut diametrically opposite should be tightened to the same degree. Each time around, each nut should be tightened a relatively small amount, and it therefore may be necessary to go around the complete set several times to obtain the correct holding-down force.

Bolts, studs and tie rods that maintain the essential working forces of the engine demand particular attention in regard to proper holding force. The more accepted method for tightening requires a predetermined stretch which maintains a safe stress in the bolt or stud and provides sufficient force for the purpose intended. Torque wrenches or hydraulic jacks are sometimes provided for this purpose. Faulty tightening, whether too loose or too tight, can cause trouble. Insufficient tightening can cause unnecessary working of parts, imposing overloads on adjacent holding-down members. Over-stressed parts may take a permanent set which eventually has the same effect as lack of proper tightening.

Instruments.—Operating personnel are cautioned against implicit reliance upon the readings of pressure gages, thermometers, meters, alarms, pyrometers, or other instruments. These instruments should be tested and calibrated from time to time in order to insure that they are reasonably accurate and that misleading information is not obtained from them.

At Idlewild Airport in New York five Diesel driven fire pumps (on the right) share load with five electric driven fire pumps (on the left) to insure protection against major airport fires.

Appendix

Useful Information

The following information is supplied for the convenience of consulting engineers and plant personnel in making preliminary estimates of various requirements of engine power plants, and is representative of good engineering practice.

Useful Formulae.—

1. Indicated Horsepower per Cylinder $= \text{ihp} = \dfrac{P \times L \times A \times N}{33000}$

    where
    P = Mean indicated pressure, psi
    L = Stroke of piston in feet
    A = Net piston area, sq in.
    N = Number of power strokes per cylinder per minute.

2. Brake Horsepower $= \text{bhp} = \dfrac{2 \times \pi \times r \times \text{rpm} \times W}{33000}$

    where
    r = Distance between the shaft center and the point of application of the weight to the brake arm in feet
    rpm = Revolutions per minute of the brake shaft
    W = Effective weight on the brake arm in lbs
    π = 3.1416.

3. Horsepower $= \text{hp} = \dfrac{P \times D^2 \times L \times \text{rpm}}{C}$

    where
    hp = Horsepower per cylinder (bhp or ihp)
    P = Mep in psi. Brake or indicated mep corresponds with bhp or ihp
    D = Diameter of cylinder bore in inches
    L = Length of stroke in inches
    *C = 1,010,000 for four-cycle engines
    *C = 505,000 for two-cycle engines.

4. Brake Mean Effective Pressure $= \text{bmep} = \dfrac{\text{bhp} \times 33000}{L \times A \times N}$

    where
    bhp = Brake horsepower per cylinder and L, A, and N are the same as mentioned in the formulae for indicated horsepower.

---

* Approximate values acceptable for computation.

5. Mean Effective Pressure $= P = \dfrac{hp \times C}{D^2 \times L \times rpm}$

where

hp $=$ Horsepower per cylinder (bhp or ihp)

P $=$ Mep in psi. Brake or indicated mep corresponds with bhp or ihp

D $=$ Diameter of cylinder bore in inches

L $=$ Length of stroke in inches

*C $= 1,010,000$ for four-cycle engines

*C $= 505,000$ for two cycle engines.

Formulae (3) and (5) may be used for engines having cylinder dimensions in metric units, with modification of constants as follows:

P $=$ Psi as before

D $=$ Diameter of cylinder bore in centimeters

L $=$ Length of stroke in centimeters

*C $= 16,500,000$ for four-cycle engines

*C $= 8,250,000$ for two-cycle engines.

6. Brake Mean Effective Pressure $=$ bmep $=$

$$\begin{bmatrix} \text{Mean indicated} \\ \text{pressure (mip)} \end{bmatrix} \times \begin{bmatrix} \text{Mechanical efficiency} \\ \text{expressed decimally} \end{bmatrix}$$

7. Torque in ft lbs $= Q = \dfrac{5252 \times hp}{rpm}$

where

hp $=$ Transmitted horsepower

rpm $=$ Rotational speed of shaft in revolutions per minute.

8. Piston Speed $=$ fpm $=$ length of stroke in feet $\times$ rpm $\times$ 2

9. Indicated Thermal Efficiency $= E_i = \dfrac{2544}{H \times w_i}$

where, for oil Diesel engines

H $=$ High heat value of fuel used

$w_i =$ Fuel consumption in lb/ihp/hr

or, for gas or for dual fuel Diesel engines

H $=$ Heat value of fuel used (hhv for fuel oil and lhv for gas fuel)

$w_i =$ Fuel consumption(ihp)hr (lb for fuel oil and cu ft for gas).

10. Brake Thermal Efficiency $= E_b = \dfrac{2544}{H \times w_b}$

where, for oil-Diesel engines

H $=$ High heat value of fuel used

$w_b =$ Fuel consumption in lb/bhp/hr.

---

* Approximate values acceptable for computation.

or, for gas or for dual fuel Diesel engines

H = Heat value of fuel used (hhv for fuel oil and lhv for gas fuel)

w_b = Fuel consumption/bhp/hr (lb for fuel oil and cu ft for gas).

11. Mechanical Efficiency in $\% = \dfrac{bhp}{ihp} \times 100$

12. Horsepower Requirements of Pumps.
Circulating water pumps, for jacket water or raw water systems, when total dynamic head is specified in feet of water.

$$hp\ input = \frac{gpm \times H}{C \times e}$$

where H is total dynamic head expressed in feet of water
C = 3960 for fresh water (62.4 lb/cu ft)
C = 3855 for salt water (64 lb/cu ft)
e = Pump efficiency, expressed decimally.

13. Lubricating Oil or Fuel Oil Pumps.

$$hp\ input = \frac{gpm \times p}{1720 \times e}$$

where p = Discharge pressure, psi
e = Pump efficiency, expressed decimally.
With the discharge head expressed in psi, the constant 1720 is independent of variations in density of the liquid pumped. Horsepower capacities of oil pump mechanical drives or electric motors must be sufficient to start the pump with cold oil, usually assumed to have a maximum viscosity of 3000 SSU. The pump size must be selected to give the required capacity with hot oil, having a viscosity assumed to be 100 SSU.

Cooling System—Capacities and Temperatures.—Pump and cooler capacities can be determined from data supplied by engine builder.

The rates of heat rejection, expressed in btu/bhp-hr should have sufficient margin to provide for a reasonable factor of safety in the selection of pumps and heat exchanger equipment. However, it is impossible to give single figures to represent the heat quantities for any general type of engine as there is variation from one design to another.

Discharge temperatures of jacket water cooling systems will vary depending on the recommendations of the engine builder. The temperature rise of water passing through the engine will vary from 15 to 20 F or less. This will determine the rate of circulation, which may be computed as follows:

$$gpm = \frac{Btu/hr}{deg\ F\ temp.\ rise \times 500}$$

Jacket water pumps should be selected with total dynamic heads of from 50 to 80 feet, as the water must pass around the tubes in the jacket water cooler and then through the engine, plus piping and valves.

Raw water pumps are usually selected for the same capacity and total dynamic head as the jacket water pumps as it is sometimes advisable to have a standby pump that can serve as either a raw or jacket water pump. In either case, due allowance should be made for the resistance of piping, valves, strainers, etc., and the final selection should be based on this, together with data from the builders of engines and heat exchangers as to the pressure drop when the required rate of flow is passing through the jackets and coolers.

The size of lubricating oil pumps, if not supplied as standard equipment (see Chapter Two), may be approximately estimated as follows:

$$gpm = \frac{Btu/hr}{deg\ F\ temp.\ rise \times 200}$$

The pump capacity selected should be in excess of estimated requirements to provide sufficient capacity for increased bearing clearances in the engine and wear in the pump. Final pump capacity should be as recommended by the engine builder.

Lubricating oil outlet temperatures will vary depending on recommendations of the engine builder. The temperature rise is generally 20-25 F.

Intake Air Requirements.—Four-cycle engines require approximately 3 to 3.5 cfm per bhp. Two-cycle engines require approximately 4 to 5 cfm per bhp.

Table 15—Fundamental Units and Constants*
(See p. 22)

No.	Unit	Abbreviation or Symbol	Definition	Precise Equivalent Values	Approximate Values Acceptable for Computation
1.	Atmosphere, One Standard (international standard)	atm	760 mm mercury at ice point and standard gravity	29.921 in. mercury at ice point and standard gravity 14.6959 psi	14.7 29.92
2.	British Thermal Unit, One	Btu	251.996 It cal.	778.26 ft-lb 0.293019 Int whr	778
3.	Calorie. One International Steam Table	It cal	1/860 International Watthour		
4.	Foot. One	ft	12/39.37 of the length of the international prototype meter (Legal Definition)		
5.	Foot-pound, One	ft-lb	Work done by 1 lb force when its point of application moves one foot in the direction of the force	0.0003765 Int whr 0.00128491 Btu	
6.	Force, One Pound	lb	A force equal to the weight of one pound mass at a place where gravity has the standard value		
7.	Gravity, Acceleration due to. Standard	g_o	32.1740 ft/sec/sec	980.665 cm/sec/sec	32.2 980
8.	Gallon, One U.S.	gal	231 cu in.		
9.	Horsepower, One U.S. or British	hp	33,000 ft-lb/min 550 ft-lb/sec	745.48 Int watts	745
10.	Horsepower, One Metric	hp	32,550 ft-lb/min 542.5 ft-lb/sec 75.0 kg-m/sec	735.3 Int watts	735
11.	Horsepower Hour, One U. S. or British	hp-hr		0.74548 Int kwhr 2544.1 Btu	0.745
12.	Inch	in.		2.5400 cm	2.54
13.	Kilowatt, One Int.	kw	1000 Int watts	3412.75 Btu/hr 737.78 ft-lb/sec	3413 738
14.	Kilowatt hour, One Int.	kwhr	1000 Int whr	3412.75 Btu 2,656,000 ft-lb	3413 2,656,000
15.	Mass, One Pound	lb	0.4535924 times the mass of the international prototype kilogram		
16.	Pressure, Unit of	p	psi	2.036 in. mercury at ice point and standard gravity	
17.	Refrigeration, One Ton	ton refr	200 Btu/min	58.6038 Int whr/min	
18.	Refrigeration, One Ton-day	ton-day refr	288,000 Btu	84389.472 Int whr	
19.	Temperature, Absolute	T	Degrees F + 459.69		Deg F + 460
20.	Watt, One Int	w	One Int Joule/sec	0.73778 ft-lb/sec 1.0003 abs w	0.738

* From ASME Code on Definitions and Values, 1945.

Table 16—Abbreviations

a-c	alternating-current
A.G.A.	American Gas Association
AIEE	American Institute of Electrical Engineers
API	American Petroleum Institute
ASA	American Standards Association
ASTM	American Society for Testing Materials
bbl	barrel(s)
bhp	brake horsepower
bhp-hr	brake horsepower-hour
bmep	brake mean effective pressure
Btu	British thermal unit(s)
C	degree(s) centigrade
cc	cubic centimeter(s)
cfm	cubic feet per minute
cu ft	cubic feet
d-c	direct-current
F	degree(s) Fahrenheit
ft	foot
ft-lb	foot-pound(s)
gal	gallon(s)
gpm	gallon(s) per minute
hhv	high heating value
hp	horsepower
hp-hr	horsepower-hour
hr	hour(s)
ihp	indicated horsepower
in.	inch(es)
kg-m	kilogram-meter
kva	kilovolt-ampere
kw	kilowatt(s)
kwhr	kilowatt hour(s)
lb	pound(s)
lb-ft^2	pound-foot^2 (feet)^2
lb/hp/hr	pound(s) per horsepower per hour
lb/kw/hr	pound(s) per kilowatt per hour
lhv	low heating value
mip	mean indicated pressure
NBFU	National Board of Fire Underwriters
psi	pound(s) per square inch
psia	pound(s) per square inch, absolute
rpm	revolutions per minute
SAE	Society of Automotive Engineers
SSF	Saybolt Seconds Furol
SSU	Saybolt Seconds Universal
Wk^2	total moment of inertia of rotating members

Three Diesel engines installed in the Cerveceria La Constancia Brewery at San Salvador, El Salvador. In the foreground is an eight-cylinder, four-cycle 400 kw generating unit.

A two-cycle Diesel 3810 kw generating set located in this plant at Decatur, Indiana, operates on residual fuel.

INDEX

**A two-cycle gas engine driven 2500 kw generating set
installed in a fertilizer plant in South America.**